D1300849

WILD WINGS

Books by Frank S. Stuart

CARAVAN FOR CHINA
CITY OF THE BEES
WILD WINGS

FRANK S. STUART

Wild Wings

McGRAW-HILL BOOK COMPANY, INC.

New York   London   Toronto

WILD WINGS

First published in the United States of America in 1952

LIBRARY OF CONGRESS CATALOG CARD NUMBER: 51-13128

Published by the McGraw-Hill Book Company, Inc.

PRINTED IN THE UNITED STATES OF AMERICA

TO EDWARD C. ASWELL

without whose generous enthusiasm for an unknown writer,
one sweltering day in New York's 1948 summer, this book
could never have been born—*In Gratitude and Affection*

PREFACE

This is an attempt to show one facet of the beauty of the world.

Wild ducks are beautiful. Sometimes, when we hear the rush of their wings and their thin, wild calling in the sky as they pass on their mysterious three-thousand-mile migration flights, there is an answering murmur in our hearts: "Oh that I had wings . . . for then would I fly away, and be at rest."

In this story, I try to take you with them.

My last book (about bees) was written also to show beauty. It has so far had nine foreign translations and is a book society choice in two countries, but it was queried in places as insufficiently technical. I would emphasize, therefore, that this is *not* a textbook on ducks, though each incident is built from actual observation by myself or much more famous naturalist friends, who have, for instance, *seen* a migrating wild duck that could not fly, being guided, as it walked northward, by its flying mate. Most naturalists know that reality is stranger and more exciting than fiction.

ACKNOWLEDGMENT

To supplement my own observations of wild ducks over many years, I have borrowed most liberally from the kindness of British and foreign naturalists too numerous to mention individually. I thank them all most sincerely for their help, without which this book could never have attained its present form, and I also wish to thank many friends among the officers and members of the following: *The Edward Grey Institute, The Wildfowlers Association, The International Wildfowl Research Institute, The British Ornithologists' Union, The Severn Wildfowl Trust, The British Trust for Ornithology.*

CONTENTS

1. The Call

THE MURMUR in the sky grew to a hiss and a roar as the flock of wild ducks zigzagged down from a great height, making for a lake fringed with dark trees. They rushed over the treetops, holding their headlong descent almost to strike the water, then, stiffening, glided a quarter of a mile without a wing-stroke, touched the lake, and so in a moment were sailing, glancing, and turning in the sunshine.

The pintail drake that had led that breathless stoop rode on into a backwater, high-reeded and still. His impetus separated him from the rest, out of their sight. Quick-breathing, muscular-bodied, his strong heart throbbing from the rushing slide down the air, his neck straight, he floated motionless, still facing the wind.

By some spontaneous rightness of time and place, he felt a sudden tremendous impulse freed in himself. He opened his slaty bill, painfully trying to utter what he felt. Meanwhile, he seemed to gather sunlight from every side till he glowed like a bird of gold. By some trick of the breeze, the lakeside grasses for a moment stopped their ballet, as if to watch. The drake, moving his head with difficulty from side to side, finally choked out a curious note, soft and mewing and rising to a stifled whistle. Then the water was gurgling past again, the grasses bowed and danced once more, the twigs on the bushes clashed in the breeze, and a fish darted below like a gleam of gold and silver sunshine being drowned.

The strange cry echoed through the reeds. Two of the wild ducks, nearer than the rest who lazily edged and dipped and floated on the lake outside, heard the call, lifted their heads, and turned toward the place from which it had sounded. They glided into the backwater and stopped, side by side, looking at the pintail drake.

He was handsome. His head was dark brown, glossed with green, and a bold white stripe ran up each cheek from his snowy chest. His powerful grayish wings were barred with bronze-green color, and his long, jaunty tail feathers stuck sharply up. He watched the newcomers in strained silence.

They provided differing contrasts. One was a pintail duck, mottled brown, youngly slender, the buff head on the slim neck anxiously alert. The other was a mallard drake, a different breed of the wild duck family. Instead of the usual dark mallard colors, however, his plumage was all white. He was as white and lovely as a swan.

Floating, closely watching each other, all displayed that absolute perfection for their purpose that birds have gained in seventy million years of evolution. Hollow and paper-light bones, clipper shape, powerful muscles—those of flight alone almost half the bird's weight; complete feather insulation against temperature and water, swift heartbeat, everything was adapted to the wild intensity that characterizes bird life. Bones "breathing" air from the lungs and sets of air sacs under the skin lightened them still further. They had extraordinarily acute hearing, and every feather had its separate sense of touch. The human eye has one center of perfect vision, but most birds have two, many have three, giving them lightning sight. And they have astounding memories: a bird, having learned to thread a complicated maze, can do so unhesitatingly if returned to it some years later. What nobody can yet tell is the point at which instinct and imitativeness in birds merges into genuine intelligence. That it does so to some degree is undeniable; there are examples of behavior, particularly in some wild ducks, which can only be described as adjustment to perceptual inference.

The peculiar cry of the pintail drake had loosed in the air over the backwater a law insistently new every Spring: "Male and female created He them." In all birds, sex controls chains of actions that direct almost the whole of their existence; rivalry early in the year moves wild ducks profoundly, but with them it is mixed with another and even more compelling desire that was now stirring intolerably in each of these three.

They rode the frilling water motionless as if asleep. But the urges and stirrings, forgotten through the half death of winter, now seemed to fill all the space between the muddy banks, swirling like trails of invisible and potent vapor and rising as high as the sky. Each bird watched the others intently, poised ready to fly or fight. Each was tense with excitement.

Each was violently aware that the choking piping of the pintail was not simply a love call, though sex shot it through. It was the first involuntary migration note. The drake had thrilled to a tiny and imperious summons that he was forced to utter. Some perfumed echo in the Spring air had entered into his hollow bones as he breathed, and stirred the feathers of his folded wings. The cry was forced by the throb of an awaking instinct. His dark hazel eyes gathered brilliant intensity as he moved his head about awkwardly, trying to utter the sound again. Staring startled about, he saw the slender female of his own breed and the stranger duck side by side. Mixed with uncoiling anger, he felt a sensation new to him. Instead of the crowding banks, for a moment he seemed to see a shoreless lake. He tasted air spiced with the scented lure of forests and alive with the stirrings of illimitable seas.

Then he looked round again at the pair who had followed him into the backwater.

With a kick of blue webbed feet, he cut across the surface, a scudding fury in gray-brown and white, the water V-ing out behind. Just as it seemed that his slaty bill must ram his white rival, the mallard slid sideways and glided out onto the lake.

Driving a great ripple shoreward, the pintail drake turned on the water. The duck remained quite indifferent. The drake drew himself up, almost standing erect on the water, curving his neck till his bill touched the snowy breast he was displaying. He tried to utter a soft mating note, but produced no sound at all despite repeated painful efforts. The duck's lambent eye observed him with cruel interest. Again, his bill opened and shut, as soundless as if he had been stricken dumb. Casually, she turned and followed the white mallard out onto the lake where all the rest were sailing.

With a violent splash, the drake flopped down and followed her. Hundreds of wild ducks were scattered about, graceful, agile, necks curved, some nervously watching for perils, the long pin tails of the male birds jauntily cocked.

The duck sailed swiftly toward the white mallard, who was idling near the side of the lake. The drake pursued her, cleaving the water. Wild ducks copy one another, and this determined passage made others raise their heads, dark and glossy,

and follow, forming a little convoy. Uneasy at the sight of so
many advancing on him, or idly exploring some new fancy of
his own, the white stranger paddled under drooping branches
through dappled shadows, doubling along the shore, and again
entered the backwater, the rest crowding after him. This time,
they did not pause in the pool of sunshine but drove through
it, breaking it into a million ripples. The white bird leading,
with the duck and then the drake followed by the others, they
turned a corner, closing in on him a little as the banks quickly
narrowed.

They were sailing straight into the wind, and the banks
were edged now with tall woven reed screens. Down the moving air, suddenly mingling with weed and mud and tree and
water smells, came a harsh scent, the very miasma of alarm.
Some of the ducks scuttered back along the water, a few rushed
screeching up the sky, but most stopped, their iridescent heads
turning fearfully, wings tensed ready to take the leap into
flight.

Then, a white dog appeared on the bank inside the reed
hurdles a little way ahead. It turned its head slightly, glanced
at the ducks, then started to sneak along, in a manner between
bravado and shame, away from the birds along the bank.

The pintail duck waited motionless. The drake behind her
poised ready to jump into the air. The mob at his back might
have been painted, so still they were. The patter of the decoy
dog's feet slowed a little as he glanced round again, as though
even his long training hardly prevented him from chasing this
mob of birds.

It was the white mallard that first moved into pursuit, his
greenish bill low and threatening, his strong orange feet shoving him smoothly forward. At this, the pintail drake drove

forward, too, with so powerful a stroke that he passed the white leader, who eyed him with an angry glitter and at once increased speed. A number of the other ducks, catching the aggressive instinct, swept up behind; the dog could not seize them on the water, and its decoy retirement whetted their avidity to mob and pursue it.

The flock now parted into two sections, a score or so swimming after the white dog, the others pausing, indecisive and uneasy. In the open water separating the two groups, the pintail duck hesitated. Then, excited by the animal's retreat, she swept forward, just as the white mallard shoved into the lead once more. They were under hooped netting now, which stretched from side to side of the perilously narrowing banks, but their whole attention was attracted by the slinking dog. Closing together, they sailed swiftly after it as it trotted away, tail and ears down, glancing calculatingly now and then at the crowding ducks, whose speed sent waves rippling out to the banks.

The dog disappeared, and simultaneously there was a noise behind them.

The pintail duck, last of the pursuers, cried out suddenly and spurted forward into the air, and instantly all of them were flying and clashing wildly along under the netting—for behind them had appeared the dreaded and enormous figure of a man. He was standing at the mouth of the tunnel net, whose wire meshes confining the fleeing mob came lower, preventing them from rising, and lower still till they whirled and tumbled into a netting pocket at the end that flung them one against another and crowded down on top of them to enmesh their wings and feet and heads.

In the panic and melee, the man was up to them now, touch-

ing them, smothering them so that their palpitating hearts
almost burst out of them, their wings struck with insane flus-
ters, and they fell over, buffeting each other, tripping and rolling among the cords, screeching and leaping and collapsing
and jerking again.

Of what followed, there remained afterward only a panic
memory that set wings lifting and hearts pounding and heads
turning to look for fear. The snaky cramping of the meshes
over and under pinned wings and seized feet; there were blows
and scaly scrapes from thrashing pinions and beating legs; the
growing heat of terror smothered till breath came thick and
hearts swelled; and then, after it seemed that the struggle had
reached its ultimate, came the hard and naked grip of the
man, poking through feathers to touch shrinking, pimpled
flesh.

In an uncontrollable convulsion to escape, those bony points
seemed to clutch and prod everywhere at once. There was
a fainting stillness while being thrust upright and pressed so
close to the man's huge body as to induce a paralysis only one
step from death, a shaking and stretching of a neck that now
alone could move, a gripping and pressing of one quivering
leg on which a steely-cold numbered ring was snapped.

2. Away!

ESCAPE! Flung into the air, a frantic and unbalanced wing-beat, a cry, recovery, and a whirling flight with shapeless terror pressing behind, up and up into the evening sky, and on as if it could never be fast enough, high enough. The woods and fields that used to be so familiar and safe went sliding by below as frightening as separate Hells. With the understanding of escape came fear of loneliness, a wheeling in the empty sky to look for company, an instinct that swung the flying bird round in a half circle over marsh and plowland and coppice to a greater lake that lay lonely and shadowed. Then, almost falling out of the clouds with fatigue and the far-reaching shadows of fear, a glide down onto the safe center of the lake.

There, tranquilly sailing, were hundreds of little shadows. As the pintail duck dropped nervously to the water, she knew she was among her own kind again, well out from treacherous land with all its prowling life. The ripples ran cool and quiet under the breast, and the darkling sky was free and open overhead.

She jerked into sudden tension, but the new sound was only that of wings whispering down the sky, and beside her dropped the pintail drake, terrified, jerky, and came to rest almost

touching her. His head was stiffly raised, looking this way and
that for danger before he would relax on the water. She stared
at him curiously with her dark eye. He had been roughly han-
dled. Even after his long flight, one vivid green tiny feather
stuck out at an angle from the edge of his wing. Something in
that soft broken feather interested her almost as powerfully as
his peculiar choking whistle of the afternoon.

Some other frightened ringed ducks were coming in after
release from the net. The night wind breathed through the
trees on the shore and lisped forgetfulness across the water's
darkened shine. But tonight, even in that familiar sound, some
whisper of the migration urge was throbbing. It made the wild
ducks stir restlessly, swimming a little, gliding noiselessly back,
circling, pausing, looking this way and that. On any other
night, they would have been happily and lazily feeding, dabbling, dipping, but all that seemed to have been forgotten.

The drake kept close to the duck, following her every time
she moved. These two were as uneasy as any. Presently, the
stars came out above, each one fitfully worshiped by its pale
water star in the lake. Some of the ducks were snatching
mouthfuls of food near the edge of the lake, but most of them
kept nervously to the middle. There were bars of shining water
and bars of velvet shadow, ripples of shimmery light and ripples of gurgling dark. Through the black and silver, silently,
the ducks drifted. The furtive, cold night smells wafted across
the lake, a running newsreel from the banks telling of life and
death and midnight love among the animals of the darkness.
Tonight, there was a new, disturbing scent of distance and of
far desires, bringing half-forgotten echoes of thin, wild voices
calling down other skies.

There were urgent little splashes and sudden ripples, stir-

rings and surgings and checks about the lake. A pigmy liquid
murmuring of water cleft by a pointed snout foretold the
coming of a swimming rat. The pintail duck glided noiselessly
out of its path, the drake following. A pale blur like a water
sprite showed unexpectedly beside them, and there was the
white drake stranger, silently sailing, watching them.

The little duck turned slightly away. She was still fretful
and nervous, and so were both the drakes. That terrifying contact with Man had left those three, and some others, an uneasy
legacy. Each now wore a metal band fastened on one scaly leg.
Clinging trailers of weed they were used to, but this cold, hard
thing would not shake off or scratch off or scrape off against
any sodden underwater branch. It was not hurtful. It made
no difference to swimming or walking or flying, but it was
there, a nuisance, an alarming reminder. Irritatedly, first one,
then another would try to kick it off. But it would not come
off. By its means, Man would identify them again one day.

As the earth hushed and the darkness deepened before
dawn, the plopplings and lipplings and feathery shufflings
about the lake slowly stilled. The moon had set. The stars were
hidden. The whispering of water on the distant shore was
silenced, for now the surface lay as quiet as black glass. The
breeze had been dying away for some time, and now, after
a sigh or two, the air became still. The creatures of the night
had curled up to rest. The first drowsy stirrings and cheepings
of daytime had not yet begun.

Each bird was rigidly awake. Every muscle was compressed
at a pin-point alert, and each separate feather thrilled. Eyes
focused intensely through the softness of the dark with that
vision, quick as in a lightning flash, that is the heritage of
birds. As they waited, there began to steal again, first through

one, then the next, that silent migration sense from beyond
their knowledge, a mulled fume of Springtime creeping northward, tugging at their senses as it passed, to take them with
it to awake the wintry northern world.

Floating absolutely motionless in the dark, the wild ducks
listened to the pigmy challenge. The sunlight that was still
far over the world's southern rim softly burnished the buds
that are the spear points of Spring's legions. In the air about
them, stirring the hearts of foetus flowers yet tight-coiled,
moved the first fragrances of a Summer afternoon still many
months south. And these secret things released a wildness
among the birds that coursed through them, fiery and thick,
stirring imprisoned forces in forgotten sex glands, stiffening
display muscles of wing and tail and neck, widening hot eyes,
and setting beating and shivering the basic pulses of life itself.

As the first thought of paleness stole about the world, the
lake seemed to explode—thousands of wild ducks together
sprang straight up into the air, with such a clashing of strong
wings as sounded like a hurricane. They began to roll away
along the lake, as it were regiment by regiment, each passing
over the rest and sweeping down behind the flock, leapfrog-
ging hundreds at a time, with an unceasing roar of sound.

The pintail duck and drake and the white drake found
themselves flying in the midst of a whirling cloud of moving
specks, rising and falling on the air, tumbling and gliding,
flying over and under each other so close as almost to touch
wings, thunderbolting down the edge of a cloud washed with
dawn pink, plunging back into the earth's shadow, then wheeling up and up till the whole red edge of the sun could be
seen bruising and flushing the eastern horizon. This dawn
flight, like most things wild, was useful as well as beautiful.

Rushing wind flowing through every feather brushed and combed away each grain of dust. Lungs, hollow bones, and air sacs under the skin in the avian body filled with the essence of the morning, and each wingbeat, giving volition through the newly warming and scenting air, increased vitality.

It was hard to leave the playing mob in the sky, but already hundreds of wild ducks were splashing and eagerly feeding below, making up for chances lost during the unnatural excitement of the night. But that excitement had projected itself into the daytime; a peculiar urgency was abroad. So out went rigid wings astretch, and the air poured past as the gliding birds dived toward the water.

Hunting for food at dawn was usually a leisured affair, a mere topping-off of the night's enjoyments. But now each bird greedily hastened, glancing this way and that, darting and scrambling uneasily to and fro as if in fear the rest might fly away. Some were preening each separate feather, passing it through a bill already filled with oily essence from the preen gland. Everywhere was a feeling of unrest.

The pair of pintails glided out into a patch of free water and began urgently to wash feathers and wings and tail, dipping heads swiftly under the cool flow of the lake, plunging and scattering drops in silver showers. They presently swam over to the shallows, drinking thirstily, then snapping at succulent pondweeds and the tips of bowing sedges and water grasses, piercing down for a swimming water beetle, tearing up a silky water plantain, pausing, staring round the shining vista where crowds of others were eating and drinking and washing and preening, and then bolting down a new bit of pondweed that slid lusciously cooling down a hungry throat.

A sudden alarm in the ghostly dawn—the murmur and

gathering roar of wings beating down the sky—and an apparently endless concourse of other wild ducks were coming in, calling, pouring down in a tremendous crowd, ruffling the leaden shield of the lake as they began to alight. Turning and tumbling with involuntary delight, pelting under and over each other, they jockeyed for places in the crowds that sat swaying and balancing on the ruffled waves of their own coming, staring round, calling to one another, challenging, dipping and splashing all over the lake.

All were wildly excited, all by one obscure instinct, the emigration desire that was flowing through the morning air with a gathering strength more pervasive than the growing light itself. Everywhere now began a stretching and testing of strong wings as birds stood up on the water and started to turn in dozens toward the north. Birds were reaching up their shining necks stiffly, then relaxing; they were crowding into the first patches of sunlight on the water and busily preening, like travelers fastening their coats before a journey.

The great flock of wild birds was still increasing as more squadrons flew in over the treetops. One common impulse had made them gather here and now struggled for definition among them all—to go away and find a new life altogether, to leave behind and abandon everything known, to pass over the horizon out of the old world into something new. All living things stir to this message that each successive Spring whispers into every waking heart, but hot-blooded, quick-breathing birds feel it with the greatest intensity of all.

It was the pintail duck that touched off, like a great explosion, all the excitement and longing, the bursting desire and quivering need of that innumerable flock of wild birds on the lake. She lifted her head sharply and remained trans-

fixed, then sprang straight up off the water with a triumphant
flash of wings as she remembered the half-choked migration
call she had heard yesterday from the pintail drake. She
climbed almost vertically; at her first wing stroke, the drake
followed her, the white mallard chased him, and it looked as
if a cloud of dust was blowing up from the steely lake, swirling, gusting, and puffing higher and higher, thickening each
moment as more and more hundreds of wild fowl leaped from
the dimness below.

The duck, climbing till she could see the whole ball of the
sun resting on the world's eastern rim, spun northward, and
as she did so, all the birds below her, pressing in general melee
up the sky, turned northward too, reaching their slender necks
forward, settling their streamlined bodies on the flowing currents of the air, and stretching to the uttermost in wingbeats.

The two drakes, gray-brown and white, moved into the lead,
the duck pressing close behind them, and thousands of wings,
throbbing to and fro five hundred times each minute, mingled
faster than eye could follow in a rhythm of swish and clash,
strike and return, hiss and flow, as the air waves went undulat-
ing by.

Far down below, the little pattern of the fields and woods
began to slide quietly past at an even, unbroken pace of almost
a mile a minute. The birds were flying in a mile-wide echelon,
the lower ones climbing steadily to reach an altitude only a
little below the leaders, yet keeping their formation so that
they traveled almost wing tip to hard-striking wing tip. As
they went, the formation closed up, following some law of air
flow and slipstream understood by those whose playground is
the upper sky. Within ten minutes, they were flying so tightly
that the uppermost birds could not have seen the ground

behind them, but only countless flying bodies hurrying along in a compulsion of instinct that nothing less than death could halt.

As the golden spangle of the distant lake tipped over the world's curved rim behind and dropped out of sight, the pin-tail drake uttered a loud fluting whistle. It wailed through the immensity of the air, and other birds took it up and echoed and flung it on so that it ran, wild and forlorn, right across the flying regiment and floated plaintively down to where the earth below was spinning itself silently into the light of a new day.

The wild ducks were crying their farewell.

3. Northern Flightway

THE SOUTH WIND blustering along in gusts behind their tails disturbed stiffly held steering feathers while it lifted and urged them onward toward the secretly magnetic and beckoning north.

They were flying purposefully, still traveling at almost a mile a minute. They shared such exulting excitement that sometimes one or two, sometimes a group, and sometimes almost all of them together would play on the sliding air waves as swimmers play in the sea. Here and there, a bird would lean sideways on the flick of a striking pinion, glide like a fish under a neighbor while closing wings suddenly to avoid collision, then stretch them again in a vacant yard of space amidst strangers whose craning necks and brilliant eyes were shining with this new northern desire. Another would soar suddenly, missing other fliers by a feather's width in inconsequent artistry, while those nearby adjusted with coordinated and careless perfection as though this aerial ballet leap had been rehearsed a thousand times.

Each individual bird, nine or ten times each second, completed a miracle of instinctive skill in the control of wingbeats, forward and downward and backward to gain velocity and lift, then turning each separate feather its own correct amount so that air could pass between them as the wings swept up again ready for the next beat. Each perfectly streamlined body pierced the air almost without frictional resistance; its tilt and poise varied every moment to effect balancing which was aided by instinctive differential action of the wings and by movements of individual tail feathers; more complex than any machine, the bird flew, as it breathed, without conscious thought. The faster they flew, the faster air flowed into lungs and bones and air sacs to lighten and hearten them. Each mile northward, passing with each minute, deepened and quickened the migration instinct that was so powerfully drawing them on. So it would go on all the time while they flew more than three thousand miles toward the Pole; then, after an interval, they would return, part of the immense tidal movement of the skies that has gone on without cessation, far, far longer than Man has been on earth.

From the moment that the wild ducks leaped from the lake on this first lap of their great flight into the north, they seemed to have become footless, belonging only to the air and knowing of nothing but wings. They had lost kinship with the crawling life of earth and become an integral part of the sunshine and the lively southern breeze. The iridescent sheen of neck and wing matched the shining blue of the immensity about them; where the air was pocketed, they glided down or soared up like tricks of light or shadow imprinted on the moving air itself.

They did not fly high—not more than a thousand feet above the fleeing fields. Sometimes, at the rush of their coming, the foreshortened figure of a laborer would turn its white blotch of face upward for a moment to watch them pass high overhead. They flew for the most part very silent, except for the great drowsy swish of wings and the aerial whisper of feathered bodies piercing through the air.

They were flying so steadily that all were enclosed within a general and intricate pattern of air waves created by their wing strokes, which most perfectly and with the least possible resistance bore them up and on. The ranks and files, groups and formations adjusted themselves continually and mechanically to catch the lift and ride the ebb of the rippled air flow those ahead of them were making, each rising on the slip-stream of its next leader, every wing stroke catching and using the small rounded pillow of air compressed and left behind as the bird in front rode over it.

As the wafting wind of passage sailed under throat and chest, each bird swept forward with rushing wingbeats, each repeating in wild, air-dancing rhythm what all the other hundreds were doing, till the flight became a sort of hypnotic orgy of common motion. All were willingly obeying the enchanting call to go north among others, stretching and flying on every side, who were also obeying it, on and on with the air waves rolling past.

They were, indeed, taking part in a movement far greater than that of the myriads of wild ducks of whom they were but one single squadron. Thousands of species and millions upon millions of individual birds share in migration, all over the world, at all times of the year; streams of migrants cross at angles or fly in opposite directions at the same time. Some of the birds fly halfway round the world, and some cross thousands of miles of ocean without alighting; but all are part of the symphony of compulsive movement that each day enmeshes the whole round earth in a whisper of ever-moving wings.

The route the wild ducks were following was no chance direction, but a way patterned exactly and discreetly, selected by their breed perhaps tens of thousands of years ago, and continually adjusted ever since. They were making north, but not on an undeviating line.

The first part of the journey was across the warmly temperate land where they had spent the Winter, and this area was well known to most of them. Amazing as it seems to consider that birds can fly three or four hundred miles in one day's migration—or perhaps much farther than that—it is still more surprising that they cover probably an equal distance on most ordinary days, making their normal flights, when they are for a few months based on one selected spot. In food hunting, in escape from enemies of land or air, or just in instinctive physical pleasure of flying, these wild ducks had ranged some hundreds of miles around their lake and knew the patterns of woods, fields, rivers, and villages as well as they knew one another.

After flying steadily for some time, they saw ahead and far below a great river whose wide and fertile valley, deep green among the lighter green countryside, ran in the direction they required, more or less north and south. This river was familiarly welcome to them all; its valley was the grand trunk road of the migration highways, used throughout the year by untold millions of birds, some huge and solitary, some tiny and as light as a handful of dust. Month in, month out, in the sky above this great valley, there were twitterings, croakings, quacks and whistles, thin little snatches of magic song, and powerfully triumphant choruses of chattering and outcries as the feathered armies flew on their unmapped ways. Some traveled at night, some by day, some in sunshine, and some in rain or cloud. On some days or nights, a huge formation passed every minute or two, flock after flock, flock above flock sometimes, as far as the eye could see, each type in its own group, all traveling steadily along between thirty and fifty-five miles an hour as a rule, sometimes in such numbers at night that the vast flying column reached from the horizon over which they came to that over which they disappeared. Birds of prey of all sorts used this aerial highway and might often be seen flying quietly along alone or in groups, almost cheek by jowl with those who would normally be their victims. Neither prey nor attackers appeared to take any notice of the others, no assaults were made, and no evasion attempted. Only, if a small bird fell out through weakness or accident, there would be a black swoop from on high, and a few spots of blood would spatter the river valley, telling of one who would fly that way no more.

On this migration road over the great river, birds performed strange antics. The little songbirds, though by nature helpless and quiet during the dark hours, mostly made their migration passages by night, so as to avoid daytime enemies. Then they would sleep, tucked away in bushes and sedges, through the daylight when normally they would be food-seeking or at play. Some types of ducks flew overland by day and over the sea by night. Some birds could feed as they flew, breaking away in orderly series from their migration wedge or pattern, gamboling to and fro catching flies and insects for a spell, then returning to the formation while others broke away to feed. Other types had to space their migration journey in such a

way as always to find food and water when alighting after
several hours' continuous flight.

Some normally flew on their way as high as three thousand
feet above the wide river below. Others, the smaller ones,
rarely exceeded one thousand feet. In stormy weather, all
came down as low as possible wherever the river valley was
fairly uninhabited, sweeping up to pass over villages that
clustered the banks. Where the river bent and wound in
its course, the birds flew straight on, only avoiding any
rising land to either side. At night, they would pass over
sleeping villages or even lighted cities. Danger came for the
low-flying small birds when misty rain was falling at night:
then they might dash headlong into a tall building, even if it
was lighted, and the next morning, numbers would be found
dead at its base. Some of the migrants who were used to people
and cities perched to rest on high city buildings, covering them
with a black myriad-dotted cluster that crouched low by day
and slept, despite the roar of traffic below.

The speed of the vast flocks of air travelers up and down this
great river valley varied according to weather and according
to the natures of bird types or individual formation leaders.
Sometimes fifty or a hundred miles was enough for one lap.
Sometimes a thousand miles would be covered in one tremendous flight, using every daylight hour and projecting far
into the night; even the tiniest birds were capable of doing
this. Some of the birds going so swiftly and steadily up and
down that river valley had crossed two thousand miles of open
sea without alighting, in some other part of their migration
wanderings. Some had crossed mountain ranges at ten or fifteen thousand feet above sea level.

The wild ducks, swinging through the sunlit air at a steady

pace that was still almost a mile a minute, saw many other feathered travelers, some in great groups, a few solitary or in small parties. There was no interchange of communion with these strangers, who kept to their own formations, generally being passed by the swifter flying ducks. The rich country sliding past below provided an ever-changing pattern of interest. Sometimes there were islands in the river or promontories striking out into it. Sometimes, it broadened out enormously, sometimes narrowed. There were ships on it, but the flying birds paid them no attention. Where clusters of roofs showed villages, the great formation of birds rose higher. They were wild and shy of anything indicating humanity; for them such things meant the roar and red death from guns.

Where the river took a great sweep, they flew straight on, coming presently over forests that were succeeded by cultivated fields. All the while, the sun shone, promising the warmth and fertility of nesting time, and the sky arching over them as they flew along gained a softer and more comforting blue as the day advanced. During the afternoon, having flown several hundred miles, the unwavering sky formation of birds saw below them a lake, set in extensive woods, through which a little river babbled on its way to join the great stream up whose valley they had come but which now was away to one side.

The little pintail duck, suddenly increasing the speed of her wingbeats, shot out in front of the two drakes who were still leading the echelon and began to dive at tremendous speed toward the lake. Instantly, the whole angle of the birds' flight altered, and they darted down with a wild whirring of wings. The glittering shield of water, which had seemed small and regular from their high altitude, rapidly expanded and

took more detailed form; a moor hen that was idling near
one bank scuttered in wildest alarm into the reeds as the sky
above her darkened at this immense invasion; then, touching
down on the water by scores and hundreds, the travelers found
themselves afloat, ringed in by grave, tall trees.

The sun was still high, and in this haven where no breath
of the light afternoon wind penetrated through the surrounding masses of the trees, there was a delicious sense of almost
swooning repose. The wild ducks, staring hastily round with
craning and shining necks, began to drink after their long
flight. They washed themselves, splashed, called and whistled
gaily. For perhaps half an hour, the lake reverberated with
joyful activity. Then, almost as if at a signal, they seemed all
to settle and rest. Some put their heads down among the feathers of their shoulders; some seemed to sleep while floating
gracefully and proudly upright. Although, very soon, there
was not a sound or a movement among the whole multitude,
except where they rose and fell almost imperceptibly with
the gentle ripples of the sunny water, yet it was apparent that
a savage alertness still inspired them in their sleep. The eyes
of a bird who sat still as a statue would peer glittering about;
without a movement, another would seem to wake and listen;
gently paddling feet, with movements instinctive as breathing,
kept all the birds safely away from suspected perils on the lake
shores.

After the incessant whirring and rush of wings through the
air, this place seemed the heart of silence and peace. They
were very tired, having sped over hundreds of miles in a few
hours, yet now there was a solace from that wild urge that had
sent them flying in the dawn. Having advanced one great stage
along their northern road, they were, for the moment, content.

The urge itself had stilled, and they rode on the water completely passive, in tune with Nature all about them, calm as
the still and cool water on which they swam, no more wanting
to fly away than did the tall trees that guarded them.

The evening came, and darkness, presently lighted by a
splendid moon that seemed to sail swiftly among fleecy clouds.
The stars glimmered. Owls hooted to one another across the
lake. Among the trees on shore, there were stirrings and mur-
murs of wild sound.

The ducks quietly awoke. Some drank. Some paddled almost noiselessly about looking for food in the shallow water
or among the groups and channeled islands of the rushes.
These rushes were mysterious in the moonlight, each brownish blade as broad as the watchful bird's face, and perhaps a
deadly enemy crouched behind any patch of them. The water-
ways, muddy and still, between the rush multitudes were
like strange shining streets, high-walled. A slippery, slime-
blackened log lay gigantic across the way and had to be
climbed over, with a little scramble of wings and feet, followed
by a marbled pose in the moonlight to listen, smell, feel, in case
the sound had carried to some killer's ears. For the night was
full of killers, somewhere there in the woods, great furry
shapes with slinking feet and snapping mouths, able to leap
enormously through the air. Even under this mud-sunken
log, there might be a snake, cold, inimical, dangerous. Or
there might be succulent food, still winter-slumbered, some
little creature that sank down here months ago in Autumn
somnolence. That flop in the water—it could be an otter,
swimming now without sound or ripple under the surface,
coming this way. A rat glides black and slippery round the
corner of a pile of mud and stares with red, venomous eye; the

duck stops, for here is an animal that might leap and rip open a bleeding throat if it is angered. It slips out of sight; but where it went, there might come a weasel, lean and sharp and silent, needing no anger to spite its attack, avid to kill merely to taste smoking blood even when sated with eating. The rushes whisper and part—and it is nothing but another duck that stands alarmed, then turns pacifically out of the path and plows up some mud with its beak, looking about for food, and so disappears again.

Overhead, huge and white passing like a ghost, goes an owl, the wind sliding silent through its turned feathers, and it strikes—there is a shrill tiny squeal of the most vindictive and dreadful ferocity that fades instantly in semiconsciousness as the rat that has just passed is pierced through and through its body with horny talons and lifted dripping into the air. The owl repasses just as silently, a fat splash of red hits the water, and the dying victim squirms feebly and utters its last choking sound, soft and muttering, as it is borne away through the spiced night sky.

The great flight of wild ducks seemed, after that first swoop through the sky, to have silenced for a time their northern urge. The lake was quiet, with ample food; new varieties of pondweeds interested them. The place was very safe, for they saw no animal foes, nor did Man come near. So many days and nights passed. Generally, in the daytime, they rested and slept, with intervals of playfulness and flights by little groups about the surrounding country. The pintail duck was closely attended by the two drakes, but neither offered any further mating display. Nor did they quarrel, though they watched each other jealously. Many of the pairs in that great assembly of birds had decided on their partners; others were still unattached. Of the latter, most of the drakes kept together in one band and the unattached ducks in another. Only in a few cases was a duck followed by two or three suitors.

Although the migration urge was dormant, it had not died. The birds watched one another continually with an air of anxiety and expectation. One cloudy afternoon, all the restlessness flared up again. In mild weather, with a faint air from the south, group after group of peacefully sleeping ducks abruptly awoke, turned about, preened themselves, swam rapidly to and fro, and craned their necks, staring at one another with startled eyes. As though a message flashed among them, they bunched closer to the center of the lake. Then, with a roar of wings, all sprang up together into the early evening sky, turning northward and rapidly assuming echelon formation.

The rush of their going, falling into the regular beat of migration flight, made a sound like a single enormous feathered deity sweeping through the evening sky.

They did not stop to feed when night fell, but rode on into the darkness. They were over the great river valley again, but now the character of the country was changed beneath them. Hills were visible, and the ground was rising toward a great watershed. In places in the faint starlight, they could see marshy flats where the river overflowed its banks into muddy desolation, bordered by barren-looking crests. Just after midnight, they descended and, after a short rest, turned to feeding and exploring. Next day, they slept, but that evening they flew on again toward the north.

It was at the next stopping place, a level valley where the torrent spread itself after passing through a gorge, that the white mallard saw the falcon.

The flock had flown most of the night, then fed and rested. After midday, the white drake became restless and soared high in the sky alone, wildly stirred by the northern urge that moved him, because of his different breed, even more sharply than the pintails with whom he was traveling. Very far above the lake, he sensed the direction in which every instinct told him to go, yet angrily felt the attraction of the pintail duck away there below him in the dark shadows of the river reeds.

That was the moment when a long-winged falcon hurtled like a thunderbolt from above and upwind, turning over and flying downward at incredible speed. The white drake saw something coming, whipped round with a frantic wingbeat; the falcon that had suddenly changed from a dot to a down-striking killer kicked out with a hind talon as sharp and strong as a knife, and the drake stretched convulsively as a puff of his own white feathers billowed into the air round his head, and a red-hot stab burned his back.

Then the falcon had gone past, plummeting away below.

4. Over the Sea

THE TERRIFIED DRAKE winged away downward at an angle as his attacker, falling so far below as to be unable to shoot up with pitch enough for a second stoop, began to circle at terrific speed up the air to try again. The white drake felt a panic impulse to climb. He knew that, as he flew down and his enemy climbed, he was submitting himself to another stab—and falcons rarely miss twice. Yet the other could outclimb him; every instinct cried out that his one chance was cover.

The falcon was overhead, turning, hurtling down again so fast that he literally whistled through the air—the white mallard raced down toward the trees but only at half that fiendish pace—the dagger foot struck just over his head as he ripped sideways in a convulsive shift, feeling on his cheek the savage wind of the blow and seeing the scaly spur stab past, actually touching the feathers above his starting eye.

Next second, he was under the trees, flinging himself head-first into the cover of the reeds and racing and flapping out of sight. Almost dead with fear, he crouched, while the killer hovered, majestically surveying the rushy expanse. The white bird had been deeply scored along the back. The wound bled and was very sore and stiff for two days and always afterward bore a ridged scar. An inch less in that sudden turn in mid-air, and he must have been pierced through and fallen dead.

When the wild ducks, once more startled by the northern urge, set out again northward, the white mallard raced into his leading place with the two pintails, able to fly there in the most strenuous part of the formation, but feeling at intervals a flick of pain where the savage dagger thrust of the falcon's talon had scored him.

The river they were following grew narrower and more turbulent. In places, it was joined by thundering torrents. The hills had become mountains, there were hardly any villages now to avoid, and the thinner air gave the birds less buoyancy. They flew with increased difficulty, as if their bodies were heavier, and the white mallard was pricked more often by the pain of his half-healed wound.

In this part of the journey, they flew only short stages of an hour or two, sometimes by day, sometimes by night. All were much more sharply stirred by the migration instinct now, and their wish was to fly into the north as fast and as far as they could go. But they were guided by weather, as well as by old habits long ago developed when the veterans among them had flown this route before and spent a day here, a night there. These older birds recognized every tree, rock, and bend of the river, while the younger ones impressed shapes and landmarks on an intense visual memory that would guide them this way again and again in other years.

At night, all recognized the star patterns which helped to keep them surely in their course when they abandoned the river's twistings and flew along valleys more directly in their northern flightway. All were restless: birds have a burningly exact time sense, and the difference in their waking time each morning as they flew farther north disturbed them while it somehow satisfied something of the urgent spirit that called them on their way.

On a morning of warm mistiness, they passed over the height of that huge watershed and began to fly down again. Stopping once or twice, but only for a few hours each time now, they sped along, presently picking up another river valley, narrow at first and full of gorges, but rapidly widening as the land below became more fertile again.

Prudently, indeed with uncanny sagacity, they selected valleys that always led into other valleys going in the right direction. Sometimes, where the big river curved, they left it, only to pick up its course again. They were following an unmarked but recognized road. Excitement now thrilled through them, every bird being sharply affected by it.

Sometimes, the great echelon would change its direction for no reason of the earth's contour, but because, plain as if they could see it, the leaders sensed that ahead of them poured a harsh upcurrent of air off a dry moorland or a stretch of sandy fields.

They had been traveling this morning for some hours, but the rhythm of the wingbeats had not varied and was as steady and precise and unhurried as at the start. Still the land below was flying back at about fifty miles an hour. But the playful place-changing that had again marked the first hour had now been replaced by a more precise method of migration journeying. It had been succeeded by a constantly purposeful rearrangement of the flying formation. A regular adjustment was now going on all the time, so that the birds on the leading edge of the echelon, taking the chief brunt of cutting a way through the air, should periodically be rested while those behind, who had flown with the aid of that skillfully directed air flow, came forward in turn. The whole formation, as it were, was turning inside out constantly, except that the three leaders kept their places.

The sun was over them, and the air warm and lively. These leaders, the duck and the two drakes, were closely watched by the orderly ranks of birds immediately behind, these being observed by those behind them again, and so on, to the rearmost birds. Each small sway of the leaders' bodies indicated a variation in air currents or a change to meet a rising thermal. Each subtle adjustment of the flight feathers as they separated or closed at the tips showed a new correction to wind pressures that were slightly altering all the time. Yet, while maintaining a general coordination, each bird instinctively made its own constantly changing flight adjustments as need arose.

Soon after midday, the leaders' steady wingbeats altered, and they began to guide a long descent. Below, the character of the country had changed. Fields and woods had given place to open saltings crawling with runnels of swift-moving water, and ahead, a shimmering leaden shine, lay the sea. Down glided that great flight of wild ducks, down to within a few feet of the ground, until it seemed that they must be going to land. Then they leveled out again, rushing along swiftly and noisily just above the wrinkled mud.

This was an immemorial point of departure for northbound migrants, who use such places as regularly as mankind uses seaports. Other migration routes from inland joined at this spot, and from here ran the grand-trunk air road across the sea. It was customary for each arriving flock to sweep low over the coast, probably so as to check with certainty either landmarks or lower air currents whose condition governed the decision whether to push on over the sea or to rest until more promising weather could be expected ahead.

As the wild ducks came whistling over the mud flats, the first tragedy of the flight occurred with horrible suddenness. Excited by the look and smell of the salt water, a pair of birds lipped raggedly away from one side of the tight formation, and the dark head of one was cleanly sheared off by an almost invisible telephone wire running out to a lighthouse on the point.

The wire thrummed, the flying body jerked with upflung wings and sploshed down into the mud; uttering a wild wail, the dead bird's mate wheeled crazily round away from the rest and circled the spot, calling loudly. She almost alighted, crying out a hoarse and wild quack, then raced after the tail of the flight, then turned back again and began to flap slowly to and fro, turning her head and looking down, calling and calling.

Not one other bird of the formation wavered, nor did the leaders at all vary their pace. The duck was left behind, peering down, then stretching her brown neck to watch the rest beating their way steadily into the distance along the northward-running coast line, rising as they went. Soon, they had diminished to a cloud of little dots, and so vanished. She could stay where she was in that empty place or take her chance of joining another convoy of wild ducks coming up the coast or die—the flight went on.

They were following the coast line now, not into every bay or out to every foaming point, but keeping it in sight all the time, for here it ran for nearly a hundred miles north. All migrants have these flightways of their own that have, in general, been followed for millions of years, and with the power of racial memory that we call instinct, they accept or recognize each opening vista of the way.

Having guided the flight to the sea, the three leaders now gave place to others who moved up into their positions as the two drakes and the duck, gliding lower, let three or four ranks pass over them before beating up into a small open space in the heart of the leading squadron. They kept together, riding the sunny and salty air, sex disturbances forgotten or merged into the desire to fly north.

Soon after the change of leadership, a less favoring wind began to blow. The southern breeze shifted a point or two toward the west, and the wild ducks made a marked flight adjustment and rearrangement of the shape of their formation so as to conpensate for the growing tendency to drift with the gusts into the east. Intensely observant, they can tell by the angle of light on the wave patterns when wind is changing, or when overland by blown patterns in grass or leaves, and so correct their course. The coast they had been following for two hours now curved sharply away, and they rose in a long, steep slant and took a line at last directly out over open sea.

The sky, which had been so springlike in pale blue, was slowly gathering a gray color that looked cold and indifferent to life. Below, the crawling sea at first showed leaden, then began to spurt with white rushes of foam. The leaders rose steadily, from a hundred feet to two hundred, four hundred, finally to about a thousand feet.

As they climbed, cloud formations like curious dark castles spread over the world's edge far behind them and took up a pursuit. The birds loosened their formation to give greater wing space if the wind grew fierce. They did not do so consciously or according to plan, but as flowers close their petals on shadowy days and open them in sunshine; as much as this, the wild ducks were a part of the air in which they flew. Presently, one of the leaders uttered a short, excited call. There was an eager craning forward. Infinitely far ahead, what looked at first like a little shadow of cloud began to define itself, as they advanced, as another flock of travelers on this aerial highway. The wild duck leaders rose higher, passing over the top of the others, now visible as wild ducks also; but they, too, quickened their wingbeats, and by common impulse the two companies swiftly formed into one great array of flying birds.

The sky was whirring with the rush of air through feathers, and whistling with striking and sliding wings. Among the newly joined squadrons immediately began a quacking chatter, shrill above the lower notes of which rose an anxious piping between the wild guides of the two parties, now all flying together in front and a little above the rest.

Suddenly, the leaders dipped sharply to meet a mass of warm air that was being squeezed upward by a line of clouds so low as almost to be rolling along the surface of the tossing sea. In a moment, all the thousands of wild ducks were riding over this hummock of warmth like a skiing party gliding over a hill. It was a maneuver at once easy and dangerous—all knew that, on the other side of that wide curve, the gathering storm would strike.

As the leaders raced down toward the ragged and dark cloud edge, they quickened their movements to a more powerful stroke, and every bird in the thousands behind immediately responded. Then they were in it, hit by a smother of glittering rain and buffeted by violent gusts of wind, but they tipped and tossed, correcting each body turn and wing thrust, riding the crisscross air currents, balancing on this one, turning on that, astoundingly avoiding the cavorting, sideslipping, and diving of their neighbors. Flying on faster than before, they stole the strength of the wind and rode on the very back of the storm.

Underneath, the sea jumped and brawled. The wind went whining along, skating into waves whose tops it chopped off and flung a hundred feet up in sparkling spume. The clouds changed color all the time, from bruised purple to shadowy indigo, and in density from mountains to smoke billows; then, abruptly glimpsed through the lens of a flashing raindrop, they became multicolored and radiant. All the time, the wild ducks fled through the billowing wind. They plunged head-long in and out of the clouds, beating up on hissing wings high over the smoking eddies and confusions of the waves. Their line, which had stretched so taut and seemly down the sky, burst in tatters before each new assault of that violent storm, but they gamboled back and were blown out of their formation places again and again like notes of music, whose haunting melody comes threading and repeating through a medley of broken sound.

The leaders' task was now to maintain height and general direction without overstraining wings already weary from nearly three hundred miles of unresting flight. In every storm, there are twisting whorls of wind, some more violent and some less, some running swift as a tide race, others broken and chopped with intrusive thrusts of powerful air, and yet others relatively smooth, curling invisibly this way and that. To find and follow these changing layers of calmer air, the wild duck leaders turned bills quickly here and there, reached out with fluttered wings, glanced at and sniffed and listened to and tasted the swirlings of the storm. Always, they were alert against the downward thrust of the sharp and cold Spring rain that burst in spray off their feathers, and they sought constantly for upspirals of the storm to combat the pressing down-slanting winds. Over the sea, there is always danger; a curling wave top can climb high and sudden toward the lowering sky, distorting the shape of the air before it, to catch and drag down a dipping wing; then the back fall of the water can in a moment swallow a careless bird down under the green seas.

A wave can strike like that with force enough to dislocate a flight muscle or break a wing, for a bird flying at almost a mile a minute adds its own dangerous momentum to the blow. And especially in storm, every bird in the formation assists its neighbor by breaking up and sharing the force of the air eddies that run so wildly about the sky.

The Spring bluster through which they struggled gathered sudden sinister intensity. The waves whipped and broke and ran oilily bigger, spume drifting off their tops and spitting high. The clouds pressed lower; the close, thick rain drove harder into the sea mist and spray. The swaying, swinging formation of the wild ducks swept across the ragged sky as a premature night smothered the afternoon. The birds' boisterous scuffle merged into the storm, a part of it like the rain, the wind, and the impetuous sea. The gale tossed them, fondled and ruffled them. Whistling and crying, they soared and sailed, beating high and gliding low, twisting, turning, but still making steadily northward through the turbulence of that spume-blown afternoon.

5. *Terror by Night*

SUDDENLY, over the splashing and broken sea horizon ahead, there appeared first a shadow, then a solid line, and finally a long, low island, reedy and desolate, in a river estuary where the lost coast returned once more into the line of the wild ducks' northern flight. With an instinct wiser than any calculation, the leaders had successfully made their first landfall.

A single piping note, clear and shrill, echoed from one of the birds and was taken up by half a dozen more. Setting their wings stiffly, they began the long glide down. Hundreds on hundreds of the birds came hissing down the stormy sky, sinking among the rushes where the sea wind wandered playing such a lonely tune. Then, for a time, after that exceptionally long and arduous oversea migration flight, they remained among the reeds, quietly resting, while the evening darkened and the wild wind blew.

The island was long, treeless, and low-lying, a silted bank, not very big and utterly desolate. Salt creeks ate into its reedy flatness, and the sea crept clucking about on mud that seemed to breathe sluggishly with the swelling and ebbing of the tides.

The throng of wild fliers, almost touching one another so closely did they crowd among the reeds, started searching

about for food. There was plenty to be found, but many of
the birds, among them the pintail pair and the white stranger
drake, were at first too weary even to eat. They rested almost
stupefied for a time, floating on the water of an inlet where
the sea breached the mud island, with high reeds partly shel-
tering them from the hard-driving, cold sea rain. At intervals,
one or other would fidget a wing to ease tired muscles into a
new position or switch tail feathers that had been so stiffly
spread for steering hundreds of miles through changing winds.

The white mallard suddenly took the air again, whirring
through the dusk off the sinuously rippling sea water. He flew
inland up the course of the river in the mouth of which the
island lay like a half-submerged whale. Swift as a part of the
same movement, the pintail duck sped after him; and with an
angry leap, the drake flung himself into the rain-filled air and
tiredly followed. Before he had gone fifty yards, a dozen more
wild ducks were coming up behind him.

Bunching into a close group, they traveled some way up
the river to a place where the water broadened widely between
clumps of stunted willow trunks. There they all came gliding
down, well out into the center of the safe open space. Immediately, they started to drink, dipping and lifting their dark
heads, staring at each other, turning suspiciously about to peer
through the sheeting rain at the river banks, gray and ghostly,
with water dripping onto water and on sodden earth from the
soaked twigs.

The pintail drake was angry and combative without knowing why. He narrowly watched the duck, who circled obediently after the white mallard wherever he swam. It was apparent that this stranger was intentionally trying to separate her
from the rest of the group. He was defeated at first by the

instinct of the rest to keep together for common safety. All the time, as they changed positions, the outermost birds watched alertly, aware every moment of possible dangers that might spring from the whole circumference of this foreign shore.

After a few minutes, having found no peril or threat, they all swam together into the shallows and began cautiously feeding, suddenly stretching snakelike necks, dabbling under the water, then springing up again to peer quickly around in the dusk. Some acted as sentries only for a minute; then they would snatch up some food while others took a turn at watching.

The white drake, ignoring the possibility of peril as he always did, edged off along the shore, beyond the farthest patrols. The little duck sailed confidingly after him, and the pintail drake, his head turning left and right in alarm, uneasily followed. He was desperately fatigued, nervous, and irritable. He needed to eat, yet dared only tear up a mouthful here and there in case the two ahead eluded him altogether in the gathering shadows. He was quarrelsome, too, because this pretty, slender female before whom he had attempted to display himself and utter a love call a week ago was not only preferring another male, but that male was not even of their breed, an intruder in the pintail flock, a strange bird to be seen and indifferently passed but not otherwise to be approached. Mallards and pintails commonly feed and fly together, but mating between the two breeds causes violent exhibitions of jealousy among birds who otherwise are often gregariously complacent to a degree.

The white drake was climbing out of the water, a shocking piece of foolhardiness in unknown country at dusk when death stalks on hairy pads about the woods, and this offense against custom still more angered the pintail drake. But the white bird shook himself and immediately excavated from under the nearest dead leaf a luscious greenish larva and gobbled it loudly. The little duck hesitated no longer but went ashore after him, hurrying close beside him where he stood with bill up savoring the morsel, and she meekly turned over a leaf or two without success. Then the two walked away together deeper into the dark forest.

They were fading out of sight a few yards away when the pintail drake, nervously glancing about in fear, scrambled ashore after them. The ground was attractive underfoot; it squelched, and the deep mold certainly harbored small hibernating things that could be deliciously eaten. The drake was almost starvingly hungry. He poked fiercely under a bit of rotten wood and discovered a snail, its shell delicately sealed with a painfully produced membranous curtain to keep out the winter cold. He eyed it for a moment like a glutton, then crushed it and swallowed it juicily down. Inspired by the titbit, he struck hard down into the fragrant earth and leaves for more such entrancing food. He excavated a spurt of leaf mold sideways and uncovered a pale, sleeping slug an inch long, swollen out with slippery translucent richness. It slid into a greedy throat and glided, cold and comforting, all the way down. Wild ducks' diet is mostly vegetable, but especially in Spring and Autumn they delight in titbits of animal food.

Alarmed, the drake lifted his dark head. The others had vanished. A faint sound told him they were to his right, and he shoved swiftly through coarse dead grass. There they were, two blacker shadows in the myriad-dripping blackness of a small clearing under a tree, busily digging, their beaks almost touching.

The pintail drake paused bewildered. Rain and drips from the tree's spreading branches pelted his feathers as the night wind stirred them. A strong instinct against fighting while on migration flight, where a hurt bird is left behind, struggled in him with a sudden furious urge to fly straight at this big white intruder. He was shot through with uncertainty because he had not yet mated or set up any demand to exclusive nesting territory, yet had begun a claim to this female by his first display gestures of yesterday.

His head reached angrily forward on his strong feathered neck, and that movement brought his eye into focus for a flash of time with something that had also moved in the darkness on the other side of the clearing. Something had changed over there beyond the pair he was watching; there had been a movement where everything now was still. It had moved, not in the curve of beauty of a blown branch, but with smooth, furred stealth, then stopped immobile as the tree trunk round which it had peered.

Several things happened at once—the drake, with sex-flamed rashness, instead of fleeing back leaped up and flew across the clearing, warning the others and distracting attention from them. They jumped directly upward, springing with wings and feet; and the red monster whose ear tip had flicked sprang through the air at them, a fox, huge, open-mouthed, striking in balked fury with a paw that raked a tuft of floating feathers from the little duck's white underside. The force of the blow beat her staggering sideways, and the fox actually curled round in mid-air and straightened like a whiplash, snapping at her beating wing. His teeth clipped traplike but missed, and he fell on his back in the wet leaves and rolled straight onto his feet, snarling up at the hissing rain into which

the three wild ducks had vanished with all the rest that had
been feeding on the river.

The drake led the rush back to the island and settled there
with wildly beating heart. His swoop across the glade in the
dark, directly at instead of away from that red and leaping
fiend, had terrified him beyond belief. He was aware that the
little duck had settled close beside him, but he associated her
with the danger he had just escaped. The white mallard was
just beyond her, apparently unaffected at having missed death
by no more than inches. Not so the duck, who swam uneasily
about in the salt creek, her head turning sharply, her wings
ready to lift at any sound, the water running cold where the
tuft of feathers had been clawed out of her.

All round them were hundreds of ducks, some sleeping,
some still feeding, foraging jerkily among the rushes for anything that might be eaten there. Great numbers had flown
inland to various points along the river. Some remained at
such places to sleep, but the greater number returned to the
safety of the island, which had been, through thousands of
years, a regular resting place for migrants. Many of the younger
birds had never seen it before, having come south the previous
Autumn by another route, but all understood its comfort and
recognized it as a sanctuary whose surrounding currents, running like sluices, prevented dread marauders of the night from
crossing from the mainland. So the birds slept, but even in
their sleep their bodies stirred and wings fluttered now and
again as the mild migration instinct stirred afresh in their
hearts.

As well as the plops of playing fishes, there were other curious noises in the darkness, cluckings and gurglings, splashes
and lollops and giant sighs, as if strange shapeless things had

crept out of the primal mud and sported or sorrowed in the island creeks. All the time, the pitiless rain teemed through the blackness onto the sea and clashed into the stooping reeds, and the wind cried mournfully across the marshes, rising now and then to a wail of infinite loneliness. The gurgle of the running tide grew less toward the dawn and seemed to tire and stand hesitant, flopping and splashing sulkily about on the mud. Then it began to ebb, only a little at first, but presently with a slow, sucking strength against which the wild ducks, in their sleep, instinctively paddled to keep their places among the wind-bent reeds.

The night seemed to alter vaguely, though yet the sky had no color at all. At that moment, between dark and day, the whisper of wings very high in the sky told of new travelers on that far-northern road. The wild ducks awoke, listening, and began to chatter in subdued notes, while far above them, unseen in the darkness, a great flight of wild geese went rushing past, heralded by their thin and magic call, crying sadder than lost souls above the sea wind's sorrow.

The ducks, hearing them, stirred in real alarm. Wild things are aware and always uneasy when others behave unnaturally. Geese usually migrate by day after feeding in the dawn. These had had no time to feed, for still the world was without form, and there was not enough light to distinguish between the chaos of water and sky.

The rain was still sheeting down as heavily as ever. Gradually, reaching from the sea toward the tidal estuary, an unpleasant pinkness began to spread from the eastern horizon. The sky, black with rain clouds that rolled and raced along before a driving wind, glowed lurid. It looked as if a monstrous fire was blowing from the world's eastern rim, out over the sea; the flames spread up the sky and glowed down a huge path across tossing waves that seemed as if tinged with blood; inland, the leafless forest through which the river crawled showed deadly black by contrast with the violent color overhead.

The wild ducks were disturbed and restless. This island was a bad place for delay. It gave little cover or shelter, and feeding inland, where the river ran through unknown forest, presented a hundred perils in each strange covert. Yet the flight north now lay over open sea where ferocious winds might rage; even the young birds making their first northward flight instinctively felt a fear of journeying on that part of the route in such weather as they knew was coming.

One of the leaders of the flight they had overtaken, an old bird who had many times flown this way, suddenly darted up the sky alone. He went to a great height, circling wide while the huge concourse below watched with stiffly held necks. He went out over the sea as if trying to sense the messages in the wind, the moving clouds, the wave patterns, and the colors in the sky. Then he turned and sped down at tremendous speed, dropping among the rushes. The waiting birds turned their heads sharply from one to another.

There would be no flight that day!

6. Oil

DISTURBED and uneasy, the great flock of wild birds spread about in groups. Some began to hunt for small crustaceans; others decided to fly up the river to wash and drink. The rain poured down steadily, and the sea was wild and gray.

The little duck kept close to the pintail drake, perhaps with some sense of seeking protection after her terror at the red killer of the night before. Or perhaps she was exercising the right of all female creatures to vary the encouragement they give to seeking males. The white mallard was arrogantly indifferent. Without taking notice of her desertion or even of her existence, he joined the same group as the two others to fly up to the feeding pool of last night. Despite the shocking experience of a few hours before, he strode ashore at once and began systematically searching every big puddle on the swampy ground under the desolate and leafless trees. He ate with gusto much more than the pintails, and was without their curious elegance, bolting his titbits as if he despised all finicking.

Some of the rest followed him ashore, but none of the others went more than a few yards into the wood. They were nervous, but he was self-sufficient and cool. He made long forays alone

45

out of sight of the rest and strutted back through the pitiless rain, every sleek feather looking gluttonously fine. His apparent satisfaction gave an impression that within the wood were foods beyond compare.

The little duck and her drake stayed on the river. They did very well in the gliding shallows, dipping down for occasional weed tips and occasionally upending with bodies submerged and tails only sticking out of the water. It was a companionable progress. Although the duck never showed any awareness of her follower, she turned in his direction whenever his hunt for food momentarily took him away from her. They found a little column of water beetles swimming frantically across the river, and not one of those shining delicacies escaped a sharing-out that was friendlily equal.

The hundreds of ducks spent almost all that day on or about the mud island, never more than a mile or two away from it, resting, idly feeding, often sleeping. About midday, a sudden and violent thunderstorm lightened and tore and clamored about them and flashed all over the sea's expanse. They cowered in their reeds, close to each other, afraid, like most wild things, of the outrage of the thunder.

The storm lasted a long time, but when it passed, the rain died away, and the evening became pale, lemon-colored, and clear. The sea, now an infinity of shining green and silver, became so smooth toward evening that the ducks could see below them the passing of a glimmering herring shoal and bubbling seaweeds bowing to and fro. As the sky reddened to sunset, the throng of wild birds rode dreamlike on a rose-swept bay, now no longer things of earth or air but part of the beauty of the singing seas.

During that quiet night, a new sound crept trespassing into

their world of peace. It began infinitely far away, a feeling rather than a sound, that came to them through the water under their breasts, faintly and disturbingly changing its lullaby caresses. All were aware of it. The sound became more audible, a rhythm murmuring through the waves and very slowly gathering intensity. Presently, at the extreme end of the shimmering sea road of moonlight that seemed to stretch out of this world, there appeared a pin point of light. This slowly approached, taking the dark and distant shape of a great ship luminous with light. It passed far out from the coast, its rows of portholes golden, smoke drifting away behind it like a splendid plume, the whirl of its thrusting propellers making the water shudder. To the ducks, it looked like a huge, argus-eyed creature swimming across the sea, and long after it had passed, swelling waves came riding in and lifted the birds and went slapping over the island mud.

As the dawn came, the mood of tranquillity faded from the flock. Mingled with impatience at the delay in their journey was a redoubled urge to push on northward to the mysterious goal that alone could quiet the urgency of the migration instinct. Mounting excitement ran from group to group; hurriedly feeding, they watched one another, quacking and whistling and stretching their wings, so that the beautiful bars of color across the feathers were splendidly displayed. The chattering, preening, and fussing as they awaited the general move into the air disturbed the pintail drake, and he was becoming increasingly resentful of the presence of the white stranger and his closeness to the pintail duck.

Suddenly turning, he swam strongly down the creek, right round the distant point of the island, as if action gave his discontent a sort of relief. He went fast along the shore, exam-

ining with eager eyes the variations in color and clearness
of the water over which he sailed, watching where mud eddies
swirled, assessing each little current, and looking by habit
rather than hungrily for small shellfish or other titbits of
food.

He was only casually aware of a very swift-running current
that curled past the snout of a mud spit and bore him racing
along an unknown side of the island. It was at that moment
that he saw the shrimps. Translucent gray, speckled with
brown, they were swimming rapidly in the current over a
stretch of sand. As he dipped to take the first one, its paddle-
like rear jerked convulsively, but too late to evade the plunge
of that slaty bill. Down it went along his throat with a rush
that sent tickling satisfaction to the tips of his feathers, and
swiftly and methodically he tried to snap up all the rest. Twisting, evading, using the current, seeking deeper water, they
fled quivering along. One—two—three—four—a dive that
missed the fifth, and then they vanished into a secret cranny on
the sandy irregularity for whose sanctuary they had been
speeding.

Aware of a peculiar coldness and heaviness, the drake looked
up. He was sailing along offshore from the island in a sheeny
iridescence that surfaced this part of the clear shine of the sea.

The drake, angry and alarmed, struck deep into the water,
sending himself shearing through tiny waves back the way
he had come. But the greenish metallic gleam seemed to
swim with him, and the water that all his life before had
lapped so comfortingly about him now struck piercing cold
at his breast and sides as if he were naked. Furious, he leaped
upward, meaning to take flight—but his wings, sopped with
something thick and heavy, stuck to his sides for a flash of

time, rose too late, dropped and stuck again as he scuttered, beating and trampling with his feet to try to get into the air, and he flopped with a resounding splash deep into scummy water. He went in as if he had been flung, a way he had never hit the water before. He twisted over with his head under, then came right side up with a terrified squawk. The immeasurable sea all about him was frightening and strange for the first time in his life, and he sat there on the water, his heart pounding, afraid to move yet with every nerve frantically warning him to get away.

The oil on the sea around him, oil carelessly jettisoned by the liner in the dawn, horribly soothed the life out of the little dancing waves and glistened with the stale glitter of a dead eye. Opening and shutting his bill, the drake began to paddle powerfully against the current that curled along so smooth and swift, parting on each side of his sodden breast feathers, trying to drag him back in its grip.

He had not troubled about the strength of this current when he sailed along it alone because, all his life, he had been free of the air. Now, as the instinct to fly where he could not swim stirred his wing muscles, he ceased to understand that suddenly he had failed in a power as natural to him as breathing. With a savage effort, he again tried to leap upward. But the heavy oiliness quite prevented him from getting his wings up in time, nor would the flight feathers spread, nor his tail feathers part for steering. Once more, he floundered, kicking spray, actually jumped into the air without any proper lift from his wings, and rolled heavily and painfully down and along the greasy water and submerged. He came up pitifully, riding on it easily enough, but smothered in oil now and utterly bewildered, afraid to do anything next.

The current was carrying him backward away from the mud island. A lifetime of water knowledge rushed instinctively to his aid without relieving the terror that gripped him, and he began to swim with quick, hard leg strokes that lifted him a little from the water and sent him gliding along, not directly in the face of the race but at an angle to it. He found he could swim and make headway, and the urgent violence of the exercise, using his utmost reserves of strength, sagacity, and skill, momentarily warmed him. Yet he soon felt an increasing dreadful chill freezing skin, bones, and muscles, where the oil had saturated the fine down that normally insulated him against the water's cold.

Foot by foot, he edged across out of the faster run of the tide race. Almost more alarming than anything else was to feel so much alone on the greatness of the sea, as though there were no more of his kind anywhere in the world. The water he had reached had lost that sucking pull and was almost still. But panic flooded him again as he found that he was working harder than ever, yet going slower than when facing the sluice. His body seemed heavy, as if he had aged suddenly to the edge of death. His wings stuck tightly down, and his body was sodden and thin, with all his lovely down dankly clinging like some icy physical blanket of fear pressing on pimpled nakedness.

Struggling exhaustedly on, he rounded the mud spit and almost collapsed in a friendly eddy of the tide that began leisurely to bear him, still faintly swimming, into the mouth of the creek where he had spent the previous night.

It was at that moment that the hundreds of wild ducks went whirring up the morning sky.

A prisoner below, he saw them spreading their wings,

stretching up, tucking their feet comfortably under them, swinging out into ranks and places, the leaders rising high ahead and wheeling with delight toward the calling north. Once more, instinct overwhelmed the dreadful new understanding that he could not fly, and he made his greatest leap, but this time his wings would not act at all, and he merely hurled himself along the sea and crashed into it again without even going under, his legs scrabbling and beating beneath him and sending the water foaming round.

High at the front of the leading edge of the echelon, the glowing white of the strange drake caught the level rays of the rising sun, and the little duck flew close beside him. The last of the migrants was up off the marsh and in the air, and the whole formation, tightening and shaping as it went, swished away northward.

He lay on the water as he had fallen, his head sunk down, his body slumped, his proud pointed tail drooped along the shimmering slime.

7. *Flight without Wings*

HE NEVER SAW the pintail duck swoop out ahead of the rest and come tearing down in a great circle, or the careless zoom of the white drake and his lazy wheel in the sky as he followed high above her. For a moment there was confusion in the skywide flying wing of birds. The front of the formation appeared to melt a little; then other leaders, craning their necks angrily and uttering shrill, eager whistles, darted into the vacant places, and the steady advance that had for one moment hesitated returned to its smooth speed once more, leaving the three truants behind and below.

A hoarse *quark* above him jerked the collapsed pintail drake as though he had been touched by a powerful shock. He stared up and became aware of the two birds, the white high above the mottled brown, circling over him.

The duck, taking no notice of her follower, darted off northward after the flock, cried out anxiously, then swooped round and back, almost touching the water beside the swimming drake and tearing away north again. He made no effort to follow. He knew inevitably now that he could not fly, that any further effort to do so might even be fatal, so sodden, cold, and heavy did he feel. He had never been conscious of his body before, but now it dragged him down and frightened him. He still could swim, but there was already an unbalanced, dangerous feeling that urged him to get out of the water onto land, though at ordinary times land seemed less safe to him than either water or air.

The duck came scuttering down on the sea between him and the mainland shore and swam swiftly and lightly toward him. Above her, only a few feet over the water, the white mallard made a whistling, graceful circle and began to sweep off northward, flying very low, in pursuit of the flock that was now a hazy cloud on the horizon.

The move was well timed, and the duck cried out miserably as she watched him go. But she turned suddenly and began to swim fast toward the mainland shore, glancing back and calling sharply. Impelled as by some force outside himself, the pintail drake kicked strongly, swimming after her, but found himself alarmingly heavy and low in the water. This made him struggle, lifting himself with his efforts; he forged painfully along, the ripples breaking sluggishly away before him. The duck jumped off the water, encouraging him to fly, but he made no effort to respond. His whole being seemed to measure the distance that still remained between him and the shore. It seemed that either he must sink with the slowly burdening weight of oil-stuck and waterlogged feathers or else the frightful strain of the effort to swim so far in that condition would kill him. His legs beat slower. His whole body was racked with pain.

The duck had spun round and was swimming again just ahead, and once more she uttered that anxious, choking *quark*. At the sound, the white mallard dropped lightly close beside her, between her and the struggling drake. He swam round her fast and gracefully, his head up, then sprang into swift flight, urging her to come; as he turned north, he uttered a persuasive and husky whisper. Her head jerked to him, her wings shivered; then she resolutely started swimming again, looking back for the sodden pintail drake to follow her.

The sea picture faded from his eyes. He ceased to remember that he was swimming toward land. He seemed to be floating on an infinitely icy and unhorizoned water, his leaden legs slowly beating, his oil-dirtied plumage sinking him lower and flatter on waves that now, each one, struck him a harder, colder blow. Only one link with life remained: the patch of speckled soft brown feathers sailing on ahead of him, magnetically dragging him on.

After a time, he felt the shallows under his feet. Slowly he staggered among the pebbles that a receding wave rolled back under him. He found himself on a shore. He would have sunk down, but with a wild cry, the duck ran close past him and lured him up the beach beyond the water line. There he did collapse, his feet fallen under him anyhow, one wing awkwardly a little outspread. He lay as if dying. Even his eyes shut.

He heard and knew that the white mallard walked close by him. Vague anger stirred in him, but he could not move. The graceful white bird shot up into the air, and as the duck watched that lovely launching, he dived urgently to her and once more swooped off toward the north. She quivered with desire, but remained, frightened, on the lonely beach.

It looked as if the pintail drake were dead. For a long time, he lay motionless. The little duck hurried agitatedly near him, then away, then back. The white mallard casually returned and alighted at her side.

Presently, the soaked figure on the beach stirred, seemed to pull itself together, and slowly staggered onto its feet. Instantly, frantic with impatience, the duck rose into the air, crying out hoarsely. She flew on at a tremendous pace about a hundred yards, keeping only a foot or two from the beach, then dropped to earth, staring back. The white stranger, mistaking her impulse, flew past her and went on far ahead before he realized that she was not still with him. Then he turned sullenly back once more.

The oil-draggled figure on the beach began to stumble slowly along, following the flight of the duck. She had not flown directly up the coast, but slightly inland. After a few struggles and a fall, he got off the beach into coarse and sedgy grass that bordered the forest and began to drag himself painfully through it.

He was a strong bird, and now he was out of the sea, the killing cold of the water on his unprotected flesh was gone, though the dawn wind was still horribly chill. Luckily, he had breakfasted liberally and added more strength from the succulent shrimps. The first slanting rays of morning sunshine comfortingly touched his back. He looked foul and staggering, his feathers blackened with oil stuck to him, and his wings draggled. Some instinct guided him through the taller sedgy grasses whose roughness began to rub tiny smears of oil off him as he struggled along.

The duck rose ahead, then came swooping back to look for him. Finding him walking northward, she swept off a further fifty yards or so, alighted, immediately took to wing again and returned to look for him once more.

The white mallard began to do some food hunting for himself, turning over leaves and poking under rotted logs.

He observed the other two furtively and also kept a vivid watch all round himself for woodland enemies. He was uneasy. He would let the others get quite a long way ahead, so that he could see only the little duck frantically soaring far in the distance, then he would rise and fly swiftly on, overtaking and passing them, and do some more idle hunting till they passed him again.

The sun rose up the sky, promising a glorious day. The sea sparkled. The woods, bare of leaves, seemed to suck strength out of earth and air. Dragging along beneath them, almost walking in his sleep, the pintail drake lurched through the thick grass. Sometimes, he stopped and shrank down against the earth for a while and would have slept or died, but the duck came wheeling about his head, urging him to walk northward. He had long forgotten the northern desire, but she burned with it for them both. Her whole body was urgent with it, yet some power stronger than reason prevented her flying in terror after the vanished flock.

Two or three times during the morning, especially when the crippled bird stopped, the white mallard swooped master-fully over her, tempting her, almost physically forcing her northward at the top of his speed. Once, after the victim below had lain still a long time, she rose very high into the air with the stranger, but as he shot away north, she circled slowly and sadly down, answering some call she could not understand and hesitating miserably.

The sun climbed to the zenith and began to descend. Still, the crippled drake was lurching and stumbling northward, knocking himself constantly on roots and branches he was too blind with fatigue to see, staggering into stones, lying collapsed, then getting up and standing swaying, and falling onward again. All the time, the bending grasses scraped at the oil on his wings and sides and chest.

In the afternoon, they came to a narrow river gurgling down into the sea.

The crippled drake sank down looking at it, and not all the circling and crying and enticing seemed able to make him go any farther. Twice, he walked up to the brim, then turned terrified away. At last, toward evening, he woke from a long torpor and saw the white mallard and the little duck riding on the water closely side by side. The picture roused him, and he surged clumsily down and pushed off toward them before realizing his own crippled state.

He found he could float, tried to lift his wings and failed. But the water was no longer deathly cold, as it had been a few hours before. It was as water always had been to him, gentle and buoyant, welcoming him and bearing him as light as a leaf on its gentle undulations.

Wearily he drank, then wildly. He felt stronger. He plucked up some juicy weeds and ate as if he never could stop. Presently, satisfied, he stared round, remembering what had brought him onto the water. The other two were sailing in the middle of the sluggish river, slowly making their way toward a protected pool half encircled by a curve of bank. Again he prepared to fly, but his wings would not properly lift. So he paddled quietly after the others, even his anger quite worn out. He merely sought a place where, with at least some safety and companionship, he might collapse into the sleep so needful, now that he no longer cared even if death itself stepped pad-footed from the bushy bank.

No night had ever seemed so long. After hours in a coma of exhaustion that was not unconsciousness but more like a

sleeping delirium of aches and fidgetings and horrors, he
suddenly awoke. The moon was full, and all the world en-
chanted. Silver trees curved through black shadows over a
coldly silver stream. A mouse, stirring the leaves, vanished
with a fairy sound. The white mallard sailed asleep in full
view. The little speckled duck was nowhere to be seen. Jerking
into startled alertness, the drake detected her, also sleeping,
prudently camouflaged to almost utter invisibility within a
great blotch of tree shadow on the water, as he was himself.
Once more, his anger roused against the stranger, whose
choice of a sleeping place out in full view openly transgressed
the first and great law of the wild, where danger for one is
almost always danger for all.

The drake suddenly felt chilled through and through. He
was stiff with cold, the piercing cold of yesterday that had
so nearly ended his life before he could swim ashore from the
sea, that unnatural cold caused by oily and no longer insulating down. Painfully, he began to swim to the bank, peering
this way and that for prowlers of the night. In the shallows
he hesitated, afraid. But the cold was mortal, and he had to
take the lesser risk. He waded stiffly out of the water and
squatted in the shelter of a tiny cavern, exactly his own size,
under the arching root of a tree. He was still only a couple of
yards from the water in case danger threatened.

The warmth of his body soon made the touch of the rooted
wood and soft earth very snug. Comfort flowed through him.
But he could not sleep. Endless pictures appeared in his consciousness, of the wild-duck formation flying high, of the oily
and iridescent sea, and of his wild struggle through marshy
grasses and over hummocks and dells and through the undergrowth of starved and wind-raked bushes.

At intervals, he dozed, then awoke feeling that dangers were all about him. Somewhere toward morning, he jerked into consciousness and immediately shrank closer and smaller into his hole. For where, before, he had faced a clear, rough escarpment to the river's edge, there was now silhouetted the silent shape of an old badger, massive and menacing as a small bear.

He was delicately and sensitively smelling the air.

8. Tornado

THE BADGER's rank scent blew in little gusts to the crouching drake, whose instinct warned him not to move a feather from that fortunate position downwind of the huge hunter. The great figure stood there, solid and coarse and hairy, the white stripe down his black face silvered in the silent moonlight, looking out across the water to where the two sleeping ducks floated.

He made no attempt to swim out to them, aware that, at the first unnatural ripple of the water of his coming, they would leap up and away. A fox would have circled and tried to float motionless downstream upon them without sound or stroke, but the badger was not so cunning as that. Only when driven hard by hunger did he try to catch and eat birds. He was half starved tonight, but not so desperate as to attempt a hopeless swim. If he could have found a duck on shore, that might have been different. He stood for a minute watching the sleeping birds and looking at the eddies of the stream to see whether they might bring his prey nearer the bank. Then he shuffled round and passed so close that the crouching drake could hear the hairy giant breathing. Then he melted almost noiselessly

away between the trees, searching for insects and small, un-
wary animals of the night.

The drake lay a long while after the last whisper of sound
had died away. Then, silently, he relaxed from his cramped
crouch and waited once more for the dark hours to pass. He
was too nervous to sleep again. When the outlines of the trees,
darkening and sharpening, told of the coming of morning, he
crept out and walked to the water. The warmth of those
cramped quarters had strengthened him.

He stood, faced with sudden fear. He wanted to fly but was
afraid to fly. Suddenly, with a choking cry, he jumped into
the air. His wings seemed to tear themselves out by the roots;
he staggered, almost hit the water, then found himself flying,
shot through with cramping pains, but beating his way up and
up toward the paling stars. Although he flew awkwardly, he
could not stop flying upward though he died for it. Joy possessed him. He opened his beak and uttered strangulated
sounds. He went on climbing to a tremendous height, exulting
in the movements after having been pinned down to earth
for so long that flying had seemed impossible ever again.

Under him, he saw the other two swiftly rising with twice
his clumsy speed. The little brown-mottled duck sped straight
up beneath him, leaned over so late that he was already turning to avoid collision, and her wings clashed light as a kiss
under his as she sped away, the white stranger violently following her. That touch spurred the pintail drake to the depths of
his consciousness, wildly aroused him, and sent him speeding
after her, for it was the first touch of mating play he had ever
experienced. At this attempt at flying speed, his tired and still
rather greasy wings almost failed him; he seemed to slip in
mid-air, whirled sideways, recovered by some miraculous

scramble, then hit the water with a clumsy splash, and went sailing on into the shallows.

He was completely exhausted for a few moments, too tired even to feed. As he came to a stop, he saw the pathetic sleek body of a drowned mouse slowly turning round and round in the current just ahead. Incontinently, he dived at it and swallowed it down. The meat revived him. This river was profuse with succulent weeds, and the drake ate and drank with increasing vigor. Then he set to work to tidy himself, working tirelessly to preen his soiled feathers, growing warmed, and feeling the strength from his night's rest filling him with new life.

When the three birds presently rose together and turned northward in the air, the drake was almost completely recovered, and flying with graceful ease to lessen as much as possible the strain of the journey ahead. There was now no sign of enmity or attraction between any of them. They flew in casual comradeship with an unconscious and indifferent beauty, small and austere in the immensity of the pale sky. They turned out to sea at once, and traveled very fast—faster than the steady pace of the echelon of the first day of the migration, as swiftly as wings could bear them when reached forward to the uttermost. For the perils of the tremendous journey north were vastly increased for so small a squadron, and an instinct for safety in numbers drove them on as hard as they could fly.

The way they should go, uncharted and unknown, and not the same as that followed by the main flight because these three had traveled some distance along the shore, called them with irresistible force that soothed only when they were directly flying toward the bird track the rest had taken and that jolted into fear, almost pain, whenever they would have veered to one side or other of the way. Following the invisible through the immensity was for them no matter of calculation, observation, or thought; and had they been taken, by force or mischance, a hundred miles to either side of the birdway and then released, they would have flown unhesitatingly back into it again. They needed no estimate of wind pressures or wave patterns, no consciousness of the pull from the earth's secretly magnetic fields. Simply obeying an urgency within themselves, they took an unmarked turning here and a diversion there, always swinging back to the north with no more reasoning in it than the compass needle has.

They flew for a long time over smooth-swelling seas lilied with sunshine. All three of them young, on previous migrations they had flown in lowly places in the great sky formations, simply following the next birds ahead. None of them knew now where or even if land lay ahead, or if perhaps this shoreless plashing went on forever. They saw never a bird, never a fish, but during that morning they sped low over a school of porpoises tumbling through the azure seas, playing with their sleek and lovely young in a bliss of innocent devotion.

In the early afternoon, that tremendous race of the three wild ducks to overtake their comrades received an abrupt check. They were flying high. Some inner sense suddenly warned them of great danger in their path, though the sky was still clear. At the same time, they grew aware of the existence of land away to one side and turned together toward it, though it was more than a hundred miles out of sight. Having passed this way before, they had received a knowledge of such land from older fliers, who had not visited it themselves but had in turn inherited from their elders a new alertness as this point was reached.

The three turned and flew very fast toward the invisible land. After a time, the northern desire tempted them to turn again, but fear swung them back. This happened several times at intervals. The diversion must be made to avoid contact with a danger whose existence on their direct route had suddenly given such strong warning of its presence. As though turned by a force beyond their control, they swooped round toward the faint blur on the horizon where lay the unknown shore. Three minutes later, they were gliding down among the excited and chattering concourse they had last seen some thirty hours earlier, vanishing into the north.

The imminence of peril that had turned them aside had faced these others also like a forbidding wall. Despite the urgency for the northlands, none dared ignore this warning. Yet the throng of wild ducks had become very restless, impatient, and frightened. The newcomers were noisily greeted, but general anxiety soon superseded that. Through the swing of the sealit air, waves of unnatural warmth came pressing, followed by douches of streaming cold. The sun still shone, but it seemed to have drawn up a thick breath from the world and to be spreading it slowly about the skies. The sea was giving off a saltier, sourer smell. The air jerked unnaturally through the grasses, and the birds, able to ignore infinitely louder sounds, could hear strange new small voices in the wind eddies that spoke to them urgently of peril. The thousand little voices of the wild creatures of the land were stilled in an unnatural hush. After perhaps an hour, these portents passed. Wild life stirred again, but with haste and hushed caution. Then came another spell of breathless uneasiness.

So it had been on this land ever since dawn, when the migrant multitude were ready to set out again on their flight.

Against such warnings from the earth and air and sea, all knew it would be death to fly, though fears spread among them as they passed the hours of their uneasy waiting.

The place where the birds were gathered was a little hill-guarded lake, cold and ice-blue, with a brawling cascade fed by the lake's hidden springs, tearing a mile down a boulder-strewn ravine into the sea. Dark evergreen trees, close rank on rank, climbed from the shore to the sky on all sides. A tiny island mirrored a group of slender silver birches in the still, deep waters on which the hundreds of wild ducks rode in uneasy sleep.

With the evening, the threat that had never come seemed to die away. But the great flock of birds remained restless all through the night. The pintail drake drowsed and rested. At intervals, sex challenges stirred in his blood; he remembered the stranger drake circling and enticing the duck to leave him when his soiled wings would not lift, and half asleep, he sidled nearer her, over the quiet water, and woke with a fierce throb as he saw a dim white form close on her other side.

They all flew up noisily at dawn and turned once more across open sea, after much anxious scouting in the sky by the leaders, and craning and chattering among the rest. The fever-ish alternations of clamminess and stifling calm that had disturbed them so much the day before had ceased, yet all of them were still uneasy at the clouded gray morning sky ahead. They flew unwillingly and only because they must. The call out of the north, stronger than their fear of death, would no longer be delayed or denied.

A significant change took place when the mob of birds flew to their traveling places as they set off that morning. Instead of the echelon like a sword in the sky, they formed at once into

a solid wedge. The shape and angle of a flight of migrants' sky
regiments vary according to prevailing winds and weather, and
for the wild ducks, this wedge shape was a rare admission of
danger. The strongest fliers took the leading edges. More than
half of them were ducks, whose lighter and slimmer bodies
gave them flying precedence, and some were muscular old
veterans who had flown this way perhaps ten or more times
on previous migrations. The formation was, as it were, cleared
for battle with the storm. At the very tip of the wedge, the pintail duck and the two attendant drakes flew almost wing tip to
wing tip with a splendid pair of leaders from the squadron
they had overtaken on the route.

They had been flying for two hours at a very fast pace, all
of them silent and intent, when a storm struck them with
hardly warning enough to permit an adjustment of wings and
tails to ride it. It was quite unpredictable, a downward-stabbing
layer of furiously moving wind slicing apart the horizontal air
masses that moved over the sea. It struck down like a knife,
bounced off the ocean, and skidded hissing across the width of
the visible world.

Luckily for the ducks, the first downthrust of that freak of
the winds missed them by half a mile, or most of them must
have been smashed into the sea. Even then, the vast disturbance of that huge rip through the world's airy casing, followed
by a violent sucking-in of broken edges of air to fill the wound,
blew up the flying formation like the explosion of a bomb.

Birds found themselves tossed everywhere in wild confusion. Some collided with others, one or two so hard as to be
hurled down into the leaping sea. The rest, blinded, buffeted,
even knocked upside down, scrambled about the whining sky
as best they could, fighting to recover balance, achieving mira-

cles in avoiding each other's wind-flung bodies, and gallantly trying to reform the shattered wedge.

The pintail drake, hit as hard as any in that sudden sky terror, met the attack with a strength he never could have mustered but for the memory of his victory over the wingless fear of two days before. He was frightened like the rest, but began to battle with a new intensity, his heart beating hard, reveling in the scooping stretch of his wing-tip feathers and the thrashing throb of his wind-levered body against the storm-flung air.

Amidst the skirts of the flying clouds, advancing in frightful majesty came the flashing base of a great thundercloud. From its approach, the other ducks fled every way, but the pintail drake, wheeling to try to avoid it, was suddenly sucked toward it by an eddy that not all his strength and skill could resist. Storm-wise, he abandoned the hopeless effort and sailed to meet it on wings outstretched. He felt himself suddenly drawn upward, thousands of feet a minute; the misty colossus of the skies sucked him up like a playmate, and there he found himself riding between the very wings of the storm. Gliding silently, very high, he saw a shattering streak of lightning run down the cloud under him and glitter among its misty caverns; just as the immensity of the thunderclap sounded, like a thunderbolt himself he winged after it, tearing at inconceivable speed almost vertically downward and suddenly leveling out again amongst the dispersed and flapping mobs of his fleeing kind.

Again the sky split with jagged flame, and while the squeal of wind and avid swish of the seas was overborne with thunder, the lightning forked down onto the water a thousand feet below and bounced up in yellow tongues that seemed to seek the fliers' ruffled, soaking breasts.

For a time that felt endless, the universe boiled in chaos. Waves burst against one another and poured a hundred feet up and blew outward into space. Clouds raced, and rain drummed. Winds shouted and marched, lifting segments of ocean into the shapes of giants; once again, it seemed that the world was without form and void, darkness was on the face of the deep, and the spirit of God moved upon the waters.

The pintail drake fought to keep in the air. Whirled and battered, he was sometimes forced so low that instinctively he had to glide and swing sideways to escape the leaping crest of the wave. Then he began doggedly climbing back through the lightning flashes and the haze into the storm-riven sky. Once he got a glimpse of the little duck, shapely and competent, riding the storm, and turning on a swishing wing, he glided close over her. As she shot by, he saw his white rival swooping from above.

He grew incredibly weary. His pointed wings seemed too narrow to bear him up. His feet uncurled because there was hardly enough strength to hold them—uncurled as if in death. The icy cold of the storm filled his hollow bones. The feathers he flicked to shake off moisture would no longer lift on his back.

Once and again, the sudden finger of the hurricane struck down toward the hungry sea, sending the ducks hurtling toward waves that opened giant foaming mouths. Each time, the birds glided away and once more fought tiredly up the rain-slashing sky. But presently the drake, wildly heeling to escape an eddy, saw a flying neighbor snatched into it, smacked down on a wave crest, rolled over and drowned beneath a smother of spume that blew off the wave top like a field of snow.

Wild lights gleamed and glittered through the water as the lightning flashed, and the electric disturbances ran across the waves from horizon to horizon. Another of the wild ducks collapsed into the sea, and another and another, as fatigue began to take its inevitable toll. The rest, still struggling north, looked like a handful of tossed motes in the gigantic uproar and confusion of the broken sky.

Impossible as it seemed, the wind steadily increased in force.

9. Whirlpool

IN THE SCREAMING of the storm, the wild ducks grew instinctively aware of the imminence of a desperate decision. They found themselves struggling with this communal urgency as if it, too, were part of the tempest. From the all-absorbing task of fighting the winds and dodging the climbing seas, they were obliged to abstract enough attention to choose between two courses, each of which was full of appalling risks.

If they persisted with their battered flight into the north toward the mainland for which they were making, few or none could reach it unless the storm soon abated, and the force of the gale was still increasing without the slightest sign of change. Another alternative existed, remembered by a few veteran fliers who had met such wild weather here before that they had been forced to use it. Away to the right of their course, a great rock stood seamed and solitary out of the bursting northern seas. In a ragged inlet under its lee, there was enough shelter to ride out the worst of a storm, but only if the wind did not change and if the storm did not persist too long.

Those who had been to the rock knew that shelter existed only on one side of it. This aroused fears in them which made

them think of the rocky island with dread. Though not in the
lifetime of any of these birds, yet many times in the race
memory of their kind on earth, migrating ducks had fled
storm-beaten to that last barren haven, only to find it a death
trap. They had ridden there on tumultuous waters for too
long, then struggled feebly on their way in a still unsated
storm, and fallen by scores and hundreds into the salt waves
to die. The diversion added considerably to their journey
toward the mainland; unless the storm abated within about
twenty-four hours, to turn aside was to go to almost certain
death. Their kinship with the air and sea taught them that
such sea storms in this place could last a long while and that
then changes of wind could bring the seas in on the only side
of the island where there was at present a little protection.

An old drake with long tail feathers that seemed, as he sped
up the sky, to thrust out a challenge to the tempest made the
decision for them. He soared up and up against the swell of a
racing cloud so that all in the tossing throng could see him,
and then he turned half across the wind and went like an
arrow slanting down on the new course. Blown groups and
formations of the birds wheeled round after him, and in a
moment the worst smiting of the wind was gone, for now they
were flying at an easier angle to its main force. Struggling
through the rain in a deadly silence of concentrated endeavor,
the formation of the wedge was reshaped. Bulging and shrinking in the gusts, it could now retain its form sufficiently to ease
some of the wild dragging of the wind by a coordinated fash-
ioning of its blusters within the patterned beat of thousands of
striking wings.

They raced along very fast and dangerously low, so that the
waves, climbing and spouting, sometimes spat spray high

enough to soak the travelers' breasts and flicker from their
wings. Before the formation had gone many miles, the rain
thickened so that horizon, clouds, even the sea just below them,
were blotted out. This added a new peril, since none of them
could see whether they were unconsciously edging lower in the
blind race for shelter, though all understood that a mistake
would dash them headlong into the tops of the waves.

The struggle went on, painfully alert instincts now replacing the sight of their eyes. Tensely receptive to sounds,
smells, and movements, they wearily struggled forward. Then,
through a gap in the boiling spume, they caught a startling
glimpse dead ahead of a black rock uprearing itself, standing
out defiant from the bursting ocean—and immediately a
sweep of cold gray rain hid it again from view.

Now came the most risky moment of the whole journey so
far. For each bird must break formation simultaneously, and
as they spread wind-blown all over the sky, each in turn must
seek a friendly skein among the twisting confusion of the air
currents, ride up on it over the high hill of naked rock, and
skate down almost vertically into the relative protection of
the bay behind.

The old drake leader went first. He was whirled up a
whistling curve of air, guiding himself with masterly swift
blows of his wings, then suddenly flicked his tail and vanished
behind the rock island as if he had been shot down. Next,
pressing almost within touch on that same whirl of wind, the
mallard drake went over fearlessly, like a white flash. Then
came an eddy from which those next lining up to shoot the
aerial rapid slipped sideways away, for to try the passage then
would have meant being flung down to hit the rocks. A whirl
behind the eddy took the pintail duck and two others over as

smoothly as down a waterfall. Then the drake fled up the air, saw the bay below him ringed in bursting spray from a reef, and almost overturned when a gust of wind hit him painfully under one wing as he dived for safety. Darting so near a rock pinnacle that he could see the runnels of rain twisting down it, he sideslipped at terrific speed and sheared through the water, kicking out with all his strength to steady himself.

They were in a natural inlet protected by a curving line of seaweed-festooned rocks that broke most of the force of the seas, though they smashed and foamed and soared in the salt air above its iron sullenness. Soon the bay was filled with the wild ducks, riding high and sweeping low on the big waves that were yet so much more steady than the vast agitation of the open sea.

Waves as big as snow-topped mountains were stepping away to the horizon and seething back again, gliding majestically apart, pausing, then smashing together with noises that reverberated to the sky. The hundreds of wild ducks, swimming almost as hard as they had flown, keeping their places within the bay behind that protecting reef, were sometimes almost blown out of the water by the immense impact of the wind, even though they had the whale-backed hump of the island to shelter them. Nothing grew on this island, no trees, no bushes, not even grass. It was a naked rock, salt-crusted, seaweed-hung, rain-scoured to its ridged bones, sun-bleached sometimes, quite unable to support life, beaten by the tides as an anvil with hammers, stubbornly holding its head above the roaring and desolate waters and able to do no more.

The flock of swimming birds, whenever they dared dip their heads, looked for and snapped up tiny cockles and marine insects, some scurrying and displaced by the surging storm

waters, some clinging as best they might in the seething shelter
of submerged rocks. The whole universe seemed to be breaking up in that storm. Through the screaming and booming
and gushing noises of the night, the wild ducks rode with
increasing restlessness and fear, trying to keep their places on
the swelling water.

Dawn came palely under broken masses of cloud that fled
before the gale. The rollers outside the bay were taller than
they had been the night before. Frightened and angry, the
birds furiously caught and smashed little crustaceans and
then allowed the mess to dribble away through the whirling
green tide. They stared frantically at the runnels of sheeting
rain that raced down the island's rocky sides in cool, silver-
gray sparkles, wind-blown into diamonded showers of spray.
A few of the birds flew up into the storm, trying to incite the
leaders to start at once for the distant mainland, but the
veterans refused to be hurried into a decision which, if faulty,
might involve them all in death.

The pintail duck, with her two drakes pressing near her
and angrily eyeing each other, made a journey along the island
side, staring at the rocks. She was so hypnotized that she failed
to notice, till it was too late, a new and more immediate peril.

That icy reluctance which the flock had felt at first against
turning aside to seek this shelter had been well grounded.
Other fears had finally been overborne by the fury of the
storm increasing until their one chance of life was to come
here, but the instinct against the place was a true warning.
For, in these violent conditions of wind and tide, there was a
whirlpool here.

The bawling of the wind and the mighty hammering of the
seas on the island, which made it shudder and hum so that at

times it seemed that the whole top might crack away from the rock, prevented the little duck from noticing, as she otherwise would have done, the subtle changing of the tide's voice as she advanced. She was reaching her long neck up to look calculatingly at the fresh-water runnels streaming down the sheer rock side under whose shadow she floated, when suddenly she felt herself seized and dragged along in the water faster than she had ever been in her life. The rock wall fled backward past her; the water was glassy green, traveling so rapidly that it looked solid, marbled with long thin streaks of foam hardly wider than hairs. The duck, to whom water had always been a playmate, tried to turn out of the rip, found she could not do so, half spun in its racing whirl, and instinctively attempted to leap up into the air out of it.

Her wings beat the air, but her feet were gripped beneath the fleeing water, and she was whirled round and dragged onward faster than ever. Then she found that her feet were so tightly held by the current that she could no longer move them even to swim. She was helpless.

The two drakes, who had been following her, sheered off with a panic splashing and flapping of wings and feet, only just in time to escape the same fate. Now, from close to the rock wall, in a silent pool, they watched the female they both desired frantically fighting for her life. She was on the outer edge of a maelstrom of green water, being dragged round at a tremendous pace between the smoothness of the rock and a group of upreared points a hundred yards away in the sea. This whirlpool spun so swiftly that it was actually lower toward its center than on its outer rim. In the middle, there was a black shining hole in the sea, down which bruised and broken shreds of sea tangle, after being whirled round in diminishing circles, suddenly glissaded over and were noisily sucked out of sight.

Spinning so that now her back was to them, now her chest, she swung in that whirl of smooth water, moving nearer the central mouth. Both drakes suddenly took wing into the storm, unable in their terror, excitement, and desire to stay on the sea. The pintail drake, blindly following an instinct that was as devoid of reasoning as if in some swift movement he tried to save his own life, attempted the only chance for the victim's escape. Halfway between the outer circle of the maelstrom and its gaping central mouth, a single needle of rock stuck a foot from the smoothed water, which divided about it, hurling up a constant spray. Diving at plummet pace through this spume almost to touch the race of the current, the drake shot up, turned, dived again at the same point, then circled high.

The little duck, still slowly spinning as she was borne faster and faster in diminishing circles, was rushed toward the rock as if she must strike it and scatter in a handful of feathers. Just as the current hesitated for a fraction of a second before twisting her to one side and on to the sucking center, she gave a convulsive upward leap, thrashing with wings and feet— and was out and flying. She went fifty yards, then fell more than alighted on the smoother water.

She was safe. Both drakes dropped at her side. For several minutes, she was unable to swim. She floated there exhausted. Then, with quick, terrified kicks, she raced back to the rest of the flock, followed by the other two.

That day whirled and blew itself away with fountains of foam and a boom of breakers, hammering on the island, that could have been heard five or six miles out to sea. Swirling, combing, and boiling, the water raced and roared; there was madness in it, something demoniacal.

The wild ducks cowered and swam in their bay. They dared not fly. Toward evening, the wind began to move in gusts a little and a little more round the island. As darkness came down, so black as to hide sea and island together, white and glimmering hundred-foot-high ghosts of foam shot upward off the rocks, and spray like maddened rain poured in great drifts across the tiredly swimming birds.

Exhausted beyond endurance by lack of sleep, draggled, too faint to attend to their feathers, the flock of wild ducks lay like dying things under the first wan glimpses of the pale sea moon. A new danger was beginning to announce itself, and though all were conscious of it, they were helpless to avert it.

The sound of the tremendous drive of the sea on the island was steadily altering. The wind was swinging round, piling the immensity of water before it on the rock from a new angle. The rollers that had been smashing at the opposite wall of the island were already racing down what had been its leeward side and running with a hungry roar along the edge of the low reef. It was useless for the birds to move round so as still to shield themselves behind the island, for on no other side was there any reef to protect them from the force of the storm-wracked sea.

About midnight, a gust of wind curved one roller in its course and shoved it, first herald of more to come, over the reef and straight at the exhausted ducks.

10. Snow

THE WHITE DRAKE, careless of danger as always, was riding farthest out of them all, under the edge of the reef that protected their little bay. In the pitchy darkness, he heard the boom as that racing wall of water hit the reef, an elemental sound that seemed to echo down and down into hollow caves under the sea. The moon was obscured by cloud, and now doubly by the curling massif of the wave as it clambered over the rocks, shutting out the sky. The white drake leaped into the air and fled through the narrowing gap as the falling wave flung itself forward and would have smothered him. The thing was over in a moment, a dozen birds that had been swimming near raced squawking out round him, but several others, moving just too late, were smashed beneath that driving weight of water, smothered, and flung forward with it as it rolled onward. Majestically, the wave advanced, flinging itself high on the rocky whaleback, then receding with a thirsty roar; and where it had reached a narrow projecting ledge, a row of sodden bodies lay, one or two still feebly moving.

All the rest of the birds, warned by the screeching flight of the white mallard and the others, found themselves in the air almost without conscious movement, buffeted and battered by the wind. Wildly circling, they saw a second roller jump the reef and flow over the bay. Exhausted, almost half dead as they were, all knew at once that to descend on the sea again would be to go down to destruction. Blown raggedly to and fro, they instinctively began to re-form for a long flight.

A sudden steely glitter of moonlight between cloud rack displayed their wretchedness with the indifference that Nature shows to all her creatures. Yet that stab of light, illuminating a thousand snowy wave tops and showing the ink-pool black of the island tightly enclosed in sky-bursting foam, really saved them. Birds cannot see well at night; it was vital for the flock to re-form closely and instantly so as to reduce to the utmost possible the attack of the wind by shaping it with thousands of steadily beating wings. Before the clouds raced over the moon face again, they had—somehow—dragged themselves into formation and headed north.

The older leaders knew that the mainland to which they must fly was a long way away. In fact, they had about a hundred miles of sea to cross, sea jumping sky-high on which descent would be immediate suicide. They had quailed before dire necessity when, strong and well fed, they had sought the shelter of the whale-back island. Now they were forced to attempt the crossing when beaten and exhausted.

The little pintail duck fought her way up the sky into the leading place, with the two drakes one on each side of her. Each was conscious of the other merely as a part of the assemblage which would be dangerously incomplete if any bird dropped out. The duck leader began to climb higher and higher off the sea. Necks were craned in protest; eyes, glittering in sudden flashes of moonlight, started crazily from feath-

ered heads. Why this extra strain when aching muscles could
hardly bear the effort of level flight? Nonetheless, all the
thousands of birds obeyed, struggling higher and higher as if
they must—two thousand feet, three thousand, higher and
higher still.

At an amazing height for storm flying, which is usually as
low as is safe, the formation followed its leader in a half turn
toward the west. This instantly relieved some of the great
stress of flight, for now the storm wind partially assisted them
instead of blowing so bitterly across their way. On a tremendous slant northwestward, the ducks speeded, borrowing pace
from the gusts, and slightly, ever so slightly, slanting down.
The miles passed, and presently that blissful ease of the long
tack was over, and they had to fight their way once more to
a position high enough to repeat the maneuver. Since climbing was heartbreaking work anyway, they turned on the other
tack, into the eye of the wind.

The effort was almost killing. But it was necessary, so as to
maintain their course to make a landfall at the nearest point.
And they were encouraged by sensing land much nearer; forty
tumultuous miles of sea had dropped behind them already
since they left the rock island. Moreover, if they could fight
their way up to a height again, they could seek blissful relief
by turning once more on a long slant partly downwind. One
rolled over, heartbroken by too much effort, and was whirled
away into the blackness of the night. Another followed. But
the rest struggled high, turned, and began to follow their
leaders northwestward once more.

So, in the end, they came to land. Alternately veiled and
uncovered in the fleeting moon gleams, they saw far ahead a
spume-clouded coast, with blusters of sea fog rolling silently

about it, and they heard the ponderous booming of the sea on tall sharp cliffs. They were flying very low, at the end of one of those long slants, and without strength to climb any more. For many miles, they had been barely skimming the wave tops, too exhausted to rise out of danger. Now, they were forced to call up the last dregs of reserve strength to soar over the cliff edge. Blindly struggling, they tried to rise. Inland, under the immense shape of a mountain, was a spruce forest, and toward this they straggled, lost to all sense of formation at last, a draggled mob of storm-beaten individuals unable to go a mile farther. They alighted on the thick sweet-smelling carpet of soft earth under the trees, clustered in mobs to try to borrow warmth from each other, and sank into a sort of coma.

When daylight came, they began to wander drunkenly about looking for water. They could not fly; they could not even eat. But the instinct that had brought them to this far-northern landfall where, through millions of years, wild ducks had come in from the ocean, had not misled them. A mountain stream, broadening and slowing before it found its way into the sea, plashed through the spruce forest less than half a mile away. The mob of birds dragged themselves to it, so feeble that they could have been picked up without being able to make a move to escape; but no enemies saw them, and soon the river was covered with them, wearily washing and avidly drinking. Those who had strength enough soon began to search for food; a few were able to fly to the coast where the sea, after the storm that was now waning in the growing day-light, had loosened millions of little shellfish from their grip on the rocks. Others of the wild ducks found food in the river or under the spruce trees.

Then, for a dreamy vista of days and nights, they rested.

Their bodies became strong again, their feathers gleamed with health. One morning, the northern desire stirred them again, and they burst into the air in one great feathered cloud and started in formation on the last long lap of their migration journey.

The sky over them now had a metallic, paler look. The air was piercingly cold. In the last day or two, the ground had hardened with iron frosts, and ice had formed at the river edges, steadily growing toward the middle. The birds had become uneasy. Food was harder to get. The world gave an impression of shrinking within itself, the winter glitter, which had never been melted by the few transient glimpses of Spring that had reached so far north, returned triumphantly again. Life-sounds died away.

Because instinct and not intelligence ruled them, the wild ducks flew on farther into the north. They were going round the coast, which was indented and broken into innumerable inlets and dotted with islands, an easy place to get food that lured them on into regions of fiercer cold.

Then came a deceptive day of sudden, hot sunshine. The frost had been intense, but the blue sky denied it, and the sun, shining hard on an island lake where they were resting, warmed the water into treacherous life. Small creatures that had been hibernating awoke and swam or crawled into the golden rays. Leaf buds uncurled. The earth gave off a new smell, a scent of life.

The white mallard drake felt this new life released within his own body. He had been sleeping with his head in his feathers, but woke with a leap as if some strange force had exploded in his breast. Nearby pintails, drowsing, stiffened in alarm, ready to take wing, but, peering about, saw nothing

new, only the ring of silent spruces guarding the steel expanse
of the lake.

The white drake sidled with a peculiar furtive motion up
to the pintail duck, who sat stiffly on the water, her head erect,
watching him. He swam restlessly about her, still with that
extraordinary nervous air. The pintail drake awoke, stared,
then propelled himself vigorously up beside the duck. The
white drake swam in front of her and suddenly bobbed his
head in a peculiar bow. The three then remained motionless,
staring at each other with starting eyes. Other pintails that
had been sleeping awoke and closed in as if fascinated, forming a circle about the three.

The white drake bobbed his head again, up and down, up
and down, in nervous, quick, almost alarming jerks. He was
offering himself as her mate, challenging any other drake to
interfere, asking her to fly with him into the air or swim away
with him into some quieter corner of the lake. The pintail
drake uttered a hoarse sound, but seemed hypnotized and
unable to move.

The white drake bowed several times quickly, now so far
down that, each time, his bill dipped in the water and came
up dripping with silver sparkles flicking off right and left. He
was excited, and the rhythm with which he swayed himself
down and up changed to a sort of wild dance. Suddenly, he
reared himself right up on the water and fully displayed his
breast, immediately dropping again and starting that nervous
bowing.

The pintail drake could not stand this and shot into action,
swimming at top speed straight at his rival, so that the angry
mallard had to swerve aside in the midst of his nodding, barely
avoiding a violent collision. The white bird, however, was so

engrossed in his own performance that he seemed quite unable
to stop it even long enough to answer that aggressive challenge.
At once, he began again, swimming round the duck with his
head drawn awkwardly back; then he darted his bill forward
under the surface and plowed it up, spurting a small jet
of water straight toward her. As he did so, a low cry, almost
a hiss, seemed to be forced from him, obviously needing
great effort to utter it, and then he stood rapidly up again
and displayed his soft white breast as before.

While the closely packed mob of pintails looked on fascinated, there came an abrupt change among the principals in
the little patch of clear water that centered the feathered circle.
First, the pintail drake repeated his rival's gesture, standing
up on the water and drawing his bill rapidly up his breast
feathers as if to call attention to them, and then another handsome pintail duck, very darkly mottled, sailed from among
the onlookers to a position equidistant between the two drakes.
Both looked sharply at her, though the smaller duck took no
notice of any of them. The newcomer glanced at the white
drake, turned a little away from him, then herself bowed to
the open space before her. It was a coquettish gesture, plainly
offered to either of the drakes, who were now sitting on the
water watching her.

The white mallard spun round with his back to her and
plainly offered his homage once more and exclusively to the
small duck, bowing and bobbing nervously and uttering that
queer sobbing whisper. As if infuriated beyond bearing, the
pintail drake flew at him across the water, a second time
causing him to jump hastily aside.

It was at that point that the little duck leapt up into the air,
followed in a flash by the other three. None of the mob of

birds who had been looking on attempted to join that flight; tacitly they admitted that this was a private affair. The little duck fled up the sky at a great pace, and the darker pintail duck got into the lead with her. Flying swiftly, the white drake followed them both, and his rival winged along immediately behind him.

With a turn sudden as if she had been shot and was falling and then recovered herself, the dark duck came round and touched the white drake with her bill and swooped away again. The maneuver was so quick that the white drake seemed mesmerized by it, and turned and followed his seducer half a mile over the treetops before he apparently realized what had happened. Then, with a furious abrupt turn, he went round in a circle toward the little pintail duck, only to see that she was dropping down onto the lake again with the other drake so close as almost to be touching her.

He went down, and the dark duck followed him. Floating on the water, the whole incident seemed forgotten. The flight had dissipated some surging emotion—for a time. Only it was noticeable that the dark duck now attached herself to the white drake and swam or flew with him wherever he went.

As that afternoon darkened toward evening, a thin and cold fog came clammily down on land and sea, and with it such a frost as the flock of wild birds had not known. The voices of the streams stilled that night as ice sheathed them in. The limbs of the trees were heard to crack with the power of the frost. Stars overhead glittered at midnight with savage brilliance. Even the sea in the rocky inlets seemed as if its heart had been frozen and ran on the cliff faces with a lifeless and oily steadiness.

The wild ducks had been desultorily feeding, but the intense cold stopped them from doing that. They crowded together in the bay where they had been hunting for shell life, and their feathers fluffed unnaturally in the gripping chill. Soon after dawn, they set off with a great whirr of wings and started to fly north.

A strange new emotion was making them all both nervous and excited. They could feel that they were very near the destination of their three-thousand-mile flight. At the same time, the sudden retreat of Spring frightened them. They had outflown the advance of the warmth and burgeoning of which their migration was a part. All sorts of powerful new urges swept through them. The mating attempt of the white drake was part of a general emotion now released among them all. Many of them had already mated; courtship displays marked every pause on their route now they were actually in the northland to which they had been so mysteriously and irresistibly drawn. Fighting was taking place between the drakes. Pairs were searching for nesting sites, not seriously yet, but profoundly stirred even when their search was more than half play.

All of them, beating their way through that crystalline air near the Arctic Circle, felt that perhaps the next stopping place would be looked upon by their leaders as that where the formation would break up and where the community would divide into families each rivaling every other. Already, birds that had flown shoulder to shoulder over almost a quarter of the world's circumference were staring hostilely as at strangers.

That morning, as they flew on, the air seemed to turn to liquid ice. The sun went in, and heavy gray clouds came piling out of the northwest. The fissured coast beneath them turned a deadly lead color, and the sea, smooth and cold, crawled as if it too would change to ice.

Then came the first snowflakes. These birds had often flown in snow before, but never in snow like this. These flakes were huge, soft, and smothering. They did not come thickly at first. They drifted about the air, from no quarter more than another. They floated very gently, flurrying here and there on casual wind eddies, and falling so lightly that they might have been down from the fliers' breasts. But when they alighted noiselessly on back or wing, they were intensely cold, and as the snow turned to water, that water pierced with its chill.

Quietly, without any hurry, the falling snow thickened. It began to sweep past and under the birds so that it blotted out the coast line they were following. On any other part of their journey, the mere sight of such snow would have sent them hurtling down to seek cover or, if they could not find cover, at least to ride out the storm on the nearest sheltered inlet or lake. Today, however, they could not do that. They were so near their mysterious destination, and now it called to them so uncontrollably, that they would have tried to fly to it through a blizzard, through gunfire, through anything. They could not stop until their own senses told them they were there.

The snow gathered power with a rapidity such as none of them in that huge formation of birds of all ages had ever seen. All landmarks vanished. The airway was blind with pouring snow that seemed to flow upward as well as down, after them, into their faces, from both sides at once. This snow had physical weight; it settled smotheringly on backs and wings and pressed them down. It enveloped those fiercely striking pinions in gentle softness, and feathers that would throw off the heaviest splashing of sea water now felt sodden and stuck. Each wing stroke needed a sudden jerking spasm of effort to throw the snow off, while other snow dropped into place so instantly it was as if the rejected burden had merely been tossed up and caught again.

Alarm changed to terror. The four leaders, for now the dark duck had attached herself to the company of the other three, simultaneously started to descend to what they expected would be the coastal sea. In the whirling of the myriad snow-flakes, they flew cautiously, afraid to strike a cliff. Then they saw, for an instant as the wind turned the falling snow, an unbroken and colossal vista of treetops growing so thick that there was no way down between them. Somehow, they must have turned off their coastal route, or else some great prom-ontory had crossed it.

It became obvious that they could not get down—they must fly on through the snow till some clearing gave them a chance to descend. But in this snow they might pass fifty clearings unseen. If a hill upreared itself in their path, they would strike the treetops and fall with broken wings and legs probably before they could see the obstacle. Or if this was perhaps a mountaintop they had seen, the land below might fall away, and in the snow they might not get another recognizable glimpse for fifty miles, a hundred.

But they could not fly much farther with this overwhelming weight of snow.

In silence, conserving every atom of their strength for the grimmest struggle of their journey, they flew on, enveloped in softly blanketing and whirling whiteness that moved so confusingly every way at once and gently covered each bird away from the rest in a thick wrapping of intensest Polar cold.

11. *Arrival*

THE SEPARATE SNOWFLAKES were as big as their heads, and so thickly clustered in the air that each seemed to touch a hundred of its neighbors as they whirled and floated, filling the whole universe on every side.

It was now far too dangerous for the whole flight of thousands of struggling birds to descend to look for an alighting place, so first one leader, then another, would beat its way out ahead of the formation and dive downward out of sight. The rest would go on with a slower wingbeat, waiting for news of what was below.

The pintail drake shot out from the rest and turned down, flying carefully on a long, shallow descent and watching with starting eyes for the first sign of earth or sea below. Instantly, he was separated from the others, they were blotted out by the snow, and the roar of their wings was silenced as if he had fallen solitary into another and noiseless world. The loneliness was terrible and outside all his experience. He was tormented by a terror that he would not find them again. Yet he flew down and down, feverishly staring.

With a convulsive whipping of wings, he turned incredibly round the immense snow-burdened spire of a tree, missed another by inches and was soaring up, his heart thumping as if it would jump out of his mouth. Nothing there but trees, trees as solidly packed as magnified grasses, trees so heavily loaded with snow that their tops looked like a rumpled white carpet. The drake fought his way up and on, splashing great sprays of snows off wings and back, stiffly stretching his neck in his agonizing desire not to be left to die alone. No sound. No sign. Only the dreadful caressing and soft deathly soothing of the heavy snow.

And then, as if he had passed through a curtain, the roar of wings and the sight of a mob of gliding bodies, a few score of extra-hard wingbeats and he was back in his place in the lead, flying hard forward. A tremor of communal fear ran through the birds. Some place to descend *must* be found, or they must drop from sheer fatigue on whatever deathly obstacles there might be. To rest—that was the thing. No matter what was below, just to stop this aching wingbeating would be worth whatever else might come.

Some time later, the white mallard shot out ahead of them and vanished in a splendid downward dive. There was always a quality of daring about him, and his very attitude, on land or sea or in the air, seemed to throw out a continual challenge. The rest flew on, slowing their pace. But he did not return. There was nothing they could do. Folly to wait too long; probably he had struck some obstacle and rolled over and over to death. The pintail duck increased for a moment the pace of her flying, but the rest held back and she too waited. And then the white drake was with them again, flying wildly. He had overshot the formation and gone on far ahead, unable to place them in the drifting snow. Then some instinct forced him to turn back. He set himself sturdily to fly on. Nothing below, then—nowhere yet to land.

All thoughts ceased as they plowed their way on, except the savage physical effort to fly, to beat off the snow, to keep height, to push somehow forward through air that seemed to have become as thick as white, flurrying mud. Presently, perhaps after a long time, the pintail duck tried to go ahead and look for a landing place. Her weary wings at first refused to alter their steady beating—only her head and neck strained hopelessly forward. Then she found herself alone in the flying snow. She was able to fly down because it was easier, so blissfully easier, than flying level. She went down only a few yards.

Something hit her a tremendous blow on the edge of a wing. She was flung round into a dark and monstrous shape that seemed to strike her over head and back and sides all at once, a sickening, shocking pain shot through her, and then snow in a solid avalanche poured onto her, enveloped her completely, and bore her down like a stone. She had hit a treetop, fallen into the huge burden of heavy snow it carried, dislodged it, and was being dragged down with it to earth.

Because she was deep in the falling snowdrift, her life was saved; she felt a thudding shock as the earth stopped her fall, but only through a foot of flying snow; with a choked outcry and absolutely frantic beating of legs and wings, she fought her way out of the smother and found herself, in a trough of snow, on the edge of a frozen lake sheeted in snow-drifted ice. She made an instant attempt to get into the air, but a shot of agony through the wing she had struck prevented her from rising.

The sound of her wing hitting the treetop had carried the

few yards to the pintail drake, who instantly and by instinct turned downward toward this bird with whom he wanted to mate. And as their leader turned, so did all the rest. He flew on forward with his own momentum and found himself out over the frozen lake, whose hard and icy surface was unevenly piled with blown drifts of snow. It was, at any rate, an open landing space, and without thought, all the ducks dropped onto it; it seemed that they could not fly forward another yard, the sight of enough room to alight robbing them of the last ounce of their powers. They more or less fell into the snow, anyhow and together, huddling in heaps for warmth, while the huge flakes filled the air above them excluding all sight of the sky.

Rapidly, silently, the snow covered them. They were warmer when completely buried in it, for then the drifting wind off the Polar icecap could pierce them no more. The pattern of their fall had placed the white drake, the dark duck, and the pintail drake together, a little apart from the rest, and now they were enclosed within a snow cavern, faintly and greenly luminous from the hard glare outside. The warmth of their three bodies melted a tiny and separate world for them, roofed and walled and floored with soft snow. All three pressed close, conscious of one another's beating hearts, together borrowing the warmth by which they were able to defy the snow. As this snow thickened without noise above them, light faded slowly, and presently their cavern became dark, almost stuffy, and their consciousness of each other was maintained only by touch.

In such situations, creatures of the wild cease to fear, do not anticipate, perhaps cease even to think. The three imprisoned birds drifted into a sort of coma that took no ac-

count of time, forgot hunger, and was blissfully rested from
fatigue. Hot-blooded and feather-insulated, they did not suffer
from cold. It was as though there were a gap in their life.

A long time later, some instinctive knowledge of the
changed condition of the outer world that they could not see
impelled them to stir. They seemed to awake. They touched
each other. The white drake and the dark duck became
sharply aware that some intangible force linked them together. The pintail drake urgently remembered the little
gray duck, and he became violently active, scrambling about
against and on top of the two others, pecking at the snow
above him, climbing up it and trampling it beneath his slaty
feet, gradually excavating upward with all the force of his
body and wings. The other two at first tried to creep out of
the range of this maniac and were smothered with kicked
snow torn from above; but presently the urge to escape com-
municated itself to them, and they began shoveling and striking in their turn, all three birds hindering one another, knocking and tumbling against one another in the darkness, but
nonetheless steadily tunneling upward and treading snow hard
under their feet into a platform that rose as they ascended.

A glimmer of palest primrose light through the snow above
showed that the surface was near and that it was daylight
outside. Next moment, the pintail drake had burst through
and, with a gigantic flapping and scrabbling, emerged on top
of the snow.

It was an amazing world in which he found himself; and
the other two tumbled up behind him to stare at it too. A
snow-burdened forest came marching down to what looked
like a huge uneven virgin snow field that rose and fell in hills
and dales of swelling, untouched whiteness. A blazing sun

shone hotly from a pale blue heaven without a cloud. There
was a motionless and complete silence, not the silence these
wild ducks were accustomed to look upon as safety, but quite
another sort of silence, immense, unimpassioned, without life.

Immediately, the pintail drake was aware that this was the
place to which he had been coming all the time and from so
far, and he opened his bill and uttered a queer, soft cry. He
knew this place as well as he knew the appearance of his own
wing tips. And yet it was completely different from the way he
knew it. When he had jumped into the air here last Autumn,
he had sped up from the surface of a lake. That lake was now
icebound, and the ice was smothered deep in snow blown into
all sorts of strange hummocks and hollows. Yet, as if his starting eyes could see through snow and ice, he could see the lake,
its hundreds of rushy mudbanks that could hardly be called
islands, its beautiful shore, the forest that came protectingly
down to it on two sides, and the vast expanse of marshland
and scrub and clustered trees into which it stretched as far
as eye could see. The trees were standing out of the snow now,
snow-covered but recognizable. Under that clump almost on
the horizon, this drake had first seen the light as he peered
through the enormous grasses that enclosed the nest where
he was born. On this lake he had learned to swim and captured
his first hunted food. Over those trees he had taken his first
shaky flights in Summer's sunlit air.

He almost jumped out of his skin as he saw the snow erupt
a few feet away, and the glossy buff head of a pintail duck
burst out of it and stare startled round, finally fixing her eyes
on his in mute enquiry. It was not the duck he was looking for,
and he turned away with an angry jerk and began to plow
through the snow. Immediately, half a dozen other heads

popped up, breaking with ludicrous suddenness the smoothness of that white expanse. The whole flock began to emerge,
leaping, hopping, half flying, jumping when they were out
with an ungovernable and indescribable air of spontaneous
delight that sent them crazily about like exploding firecrack-
ers, amidst a growing ecstatic whistling, quacking, and thrashing of wings.

They had arrived!

All the perils and strains of the three-thousand-mile journey
were past. More; the air round them was vibrant and madden-
ing with the feeling of something new in life, some unknown
extension, some undreamed-of and delicious pleasure that
made the pairs stare wildly at each other and caused unmated
drakes to struggle terrifically through the snow looking at
ducks, closing up near them, eyeing each other with fiercest
anger. It was as if a new current of some extra sort of life had
been released in them and was pouring hotly through their
bodies needing some strange outlet.

The pintail drake who had helped to lead the migration
flight rushed and stumbled faster than any among the unmated ducks. His trail left a deep plowed furrow in the snow,
zigzagging to and fro. He came suddenly face to face with the
white drake, behind whom the dark duck waited, and the
pintail rushed at them savagely. The white drake stood his
ground insolently, even started forward at the last moment to
meet his enemy, and they crashed together, the white drake
being sent rolling over by the other's greater impetus and
raging force. The dark duck leaped up into the air quacking
and alighted; the pintail drake staggered on past them, searching, frantic, shaking his shining head.

He went blindly among hundreds of birds that had dug

their way out of the snow. Some of them were flying, performing extraordinary acrobatics in the warm sky over the snow
field, unable to keep on the ground in the excess of their
excitement. All recognized this place; it was theirs, untres-
passed by other creatures; year after year, they returned here,
and to them this expanse of marshy lakeland was full of all
the pleasures. They felt the burning desires of mating here;
they had watched nestlings playing here; this was the place
that represented, to them, all the drowsy warmth and indo-
lence and plenty of Summer; they had never known Summer
away from this marshland, and to them, despite its present
snowy surface, it *was* Summer, spicy Summer food, lovely
Summer nights, playful, endless Summer days.

The pintail drake stretched his neck anxiously upward,
watching the fliers circling, diving, and climbing in the sun-
drenched air. He took a last swift look round among the
hundreds of birds playing on the ground. Then he, too, was
in the air, soaring up and up, flying after this duck or that
one and angrily turning away, staring down to try to identify
her among the moving dots on the snow.

Then he saw her, far away, solitary; from where he was
flying, she seemed hardly bigger than a sparrow, but he knew
by some sense other than sight that it was she. She lay still,
on the extreme edge of the snow-field lake, under the tree she
had struck.

Turning in the air with such a rush that his wings whistled,
he flew to her, bolting across the sky and dropping at her
side. She was crouched in the snow; he saw her bright eyes
looking at him, and excitement rushed through him. The
duck had strained a wing muscle in that violent collision with
the branch, but luckily the wing itself was not broken. She

had been able to scramble out of the snow, like the rest, but she was afraid to take wing.

Now it was his turn to try to encourage her to fly. He jumped up and swooped a few yards through the air, then circled back and alighted beside her. Again she looked at him with that strange, intent regard. He felt a mighty need to persuade her to swim, to get to water and float with him secretly and alone. To find water, they must fly.

He struggled through the snow, touched her with his bill, then took wing. Throwing off the terror that the blow of the tree had rooted in her brain, she jumped upward and found herself flying, awkwardly, in pain, yet joyously as ever she had flown in her life. The damaged wing hurt with every beat, a repeated pain nine times every second as her wing struck, hundreds of times a minute. Still, she was flying, slowly and limpingly, but flying, and the pintail drake flew with her.

They went across the assemblage of birds, some of whom were flying, some sitting on the snow. As they went, they saw far ahead of them a crowded concourse of wild ducks clustered tightly about a black mark on the snow.

In the center of the lake, the water either had not completely frozen or was thawing in the powerful sunshine. There was a jagged-edged water hole there, with heaps of snow round it. On the snow and splashing and playing in the water were dozens of pintails, every movement and pose expressive of the uttermost wild delight. For this water hole was the very crux and center of what they had flown three thousand miles to seek. This clean, virgin place was the land of their desires; this little pool, already significantly cracked at the edges as a shell cracks when its occupant begins to peck a way out, was the matrix from which the whole world of their pleasures would open.

The duck and the drake alighted together on the snow and plunged into the crowded little patch of water. He at once stood up on the water, drawing his bill up his snowy breast, uttered a soft mewing note, then sat very still watching her. Immediately, in reply, she bowed a little, her head bending shyly or carelessly, half toward him. Then she turned swiftly away and swam across the open water. He pursued strongly.

The water was icy and clear. The sky was now deep blue. The sun beat down with full summer power, and silently the cracks in the ice edge extended. The air, clean of all taint and fresh from the Pole, was wildly exciting and exhilarating. All about them curved the masses of the trees.

These wild birds had come home.

Suddenly, there was a powerful whirr of wings through the sky, and the white drake shot down onto the water, shoving boldly among the crowded birds and forcing them to make way for him. He plunged up to the pintail pair, and the dark drake faced him at once, hard and menacing.

12. Mating

THE WHITE DRAKE was by nature impulsive and bold. He instantly made his purpose clear by a stiff bow to the pintail duck, his greenish bill dipping in the water, the upward jerk of it after spraying her breast. This was a warning claim that she was his—if she would have him—and that no other drake must interfere.

Promptly, the pintail drake drove hard at his rival, spurring through the water, his bill low and pointing straight at the other's breast. There was a clash as they struck, each with the force of a snakelike muscular neck driving the ramlike bill. Each sheared away from the other, swiftly turned, and stared at the pintail duck whose privilege it was to show her preference and so avoid further fighting. The other birds on that little sheet of water, among the ice and snow of the Arctic, backed away, leaving the three by themselves and watching them closely for the next move.

The white mallard, tense with excitement, dipped his bill again, and exactly as he did so, the pintail drake stood up on the water by him, close to the little duck, and displayed his chest, his long neck doubled in graceful curves; but the gesture was simultaneously one of contempt, a gamin trick, for in

99

achieving his stance he scuffed his feet in the water and scrambled a fountain of it over the bending mallard's head. The mallard came up, dripping and furious, and with a kick of his strong legs circled swift as a cat and cut between the duck and the pintail drake. As though distressed at having been soused, he uttered, almost touching her, a low cry, half whisper, half groan, throwing his head back as if it cost him a supreme effort to produce that soft, seductive sound.

The pintail tried to edge between him and the duck, but they were so close that this was impossible without roughly forcing himself against the duck, which he dared not do. The white drake, shining and beautiful, lowered his breast and raised his tail two or three times in quick succession, the little duck looking on apparently without interest, yet not withdrawing herself at all even when his feathers touched and pressed hers. He threw up his head rapidly with feathers puffed out. Suddenly, he turned aside, stretched his neck awkwardly with his throat just off the water, then swam away at great speed for a few yards as if he could no longer keep still, straightening up as he did so.

He spun round, as if waiting for the duck to give him now a sign of approval or encouragement. All he saw was the pintail drake's back, who had instantly inserted himself between his rival and the duck the moment the other turned away. The pintail was stiffening himself with his chocolate head high and slowly turning himself about so that the duck could see his splendid coloring. As he turned, he uttered a thrilling double whistle like the sharp touches of a bow on a violin.

The duck looked critically at him, the gaze of her shining brown eyes gathering sharpest intensity in a way completely new. Hitherto, she had been aware of him, and of the white drake as companions, as personal followers, but not as anything more. Now instinct told her she must choose one or other as her mate. She watched the fine high poise of the pintail drake's dark head, his hind neck of blackish-brown, the vivid white stripes that ran up each side of his head, the hard gray-blue bill black along the ridge with an elongated black spot at its base, his sensitive and wild eyes, the grayish back, long wings and the vivid bronze-green speculum upon them. This patch of startling color seemed to attract her especial attention, and the drake, as if he knew that here was something his rival had not got, stopped in his slow pirouette on the water. The lovely color was bordered with buff above and black and white below. It glowed in the hot Arctic sunshine like a jewel. The duck noted his slender strength, the muscular curve of his neck, his powerful, lean body.

Then something like a whirlwind struck him, there was a smother of spray, and the white drake was fiercely shoving him aside once more. This time, however, the intruder was met with a lightning drive from that slaty bill, and each staggered aside.

Then came an interruption which, for a while, put an end to the display of rivalry and desire. In a moment, the entire sky over the lake was filled with a greater multitude of birds than the ducks had ever seen together in one place before. A wedge of flying bodies so vast that it stretched away to the horizon on each side and seemed to pour over the world's edge was passing over them, coming rapidly down toward the snow-covered marsh into which the lake opened out.

The noise they made was stupendous, almost terrifying. They seemed to shut out the light of the sky. Steadily, they

flew on and down, long necks craned forward, great wings
beating, long bodies stretched out on the air. Already, the
leaders were alighting more than two miles ahead, and like
some gigantic dust storm, unimaginable numbers of others
were pouring through the air toward the landing place.

They were blue geese, and beside that sudden and overwhelming army of the clouds, the thousands of wild ducks
seemed only an outlier squadron. They were on their migration way, and indeed within a short flight of their nesting
country. Deadly weary after a tremendous journey from the
south, they clustered all over the marsh as if some further
mighty snowfall had dropped on the expanse of melting snow
already there.

Too tired to feed or even to drink, too weary to move once
they had alighted, they crouched in groups so crowded as to
stupefy the eye. When all had landed, they covered a marshland area more than three miles long and a mile wide. There
were more than two million geese, squatting, breathing hard,
their feathered backs stirring, their eyes dulling as they sank
into helpless sleep.

Presently, when they had rested a short time, they started
by hundreds and thousands to look about for drink and reeds
and rushes to eat. There were geese paddling on melting pools
of snow, geese who had broken through the cracking ice and
swam in patches of open water, geese sitting asleep on mudbanks, geese waddling and shoving about importantly among
the rest, acres and acres of geese preening and peering, crouching and stretching. Something alarmed them during the afternoon—perhaps a prowling fox. Tens of thousands of them
flapped and struggled into the air, yelling an incredible and
deafening chorus, their thrashing wings utterly splintering

and rending the large Polar sky with a cacophony of sound
that would have put a bear to flight.

They stayed on the lake only a few hours and then in uncontrollable impatience flew off on the last lap of their journey. When they went, it seemed as if the skies had broken
into millions of whirling and whirring atoms, and long after
they had disappeared from sight, a ghostly whisper came back.

The suddenness and vastness of this invasion had put an
abrupt end to the courtship display of the rival drakes. They
were overwhelmed by the presence of so many strange birds
so near them, and all the wild ducks went about their affairs
almost furtively, carefully keeping away from the blue geese.
There was relief when they had gone.

The summer sun of that day melted the snow into great
lagoons and patches of swampy mud. On the lake, the ice
cracked in all directions, and first one or two, then a score of
pools opened, in which the ducks dabbled joyously. The land
steamed. There was an impression of swelling growth, as
though the buds on the trees and the myriad green things
pushing their way through the rich slime could not burgeon
fast enough. The place was crawling with marsh life, so that
the wild ducks, after the urgent and chance foods of their
great journey, were able to set about seriously stuffing themselves with everything delicious.

Late in the day, after the geese had gone and a feeling of
safety and normality was returning, the pintail duck flew up
and began playing in the air for sheer delight. Before she was
a foot off the ground, the two drakes were following, and
wherever she circled or climbed or dived, whether she shot
through the high heavens or skimmed only inches off the
ground, they raced to be near her. She would not allow either

of them to come close enough to touch her in mid-air, though first one and then the other attempted to do so. She would not play with them as they flew, taking apparently little notice, except sometimes, with deliberate cruelty, to tear round a bluff of trees and try to hide from both of them. She never succeeded; perhaps her attempts were not serious; but she would not allow them too close and showed not the slightest preference for one or the other. In sudden air tactics, she was unquestionably the master of them both. The mallard was too heavy, though he was very strong; the pintail, quicker on the turn than his rival and able in straight flight to equal or overtake the duck, was yet unable to change direction as she did, go up or down without warning, or skid round an obstacle so close that it seemed that it must break an outstretched wing.

The two drakes became mortally tired, far more tired than on most of the long migration days. Neither, however, dared abandon the chase to the other, and after a while they were struggling to achieve aerobatics with a sickening and hateful weariness. As they flipped and wheeled and leaped over the lake and the swamp, they saw below them many such courtship displays as they had between them attempted that morning.

Also, they saw scores of birds anxiously and eagerly flying about together, poking among the reeds and grasses and at the bottoms of clumps of bushes, looking for the best nest sites. This filled all three with a horrible sense of urgency. Even the little duck felt it, and it made her more shrewish and evasive than before. When at last she descended into a patch of muddy water, still with floating lumps of ice in it, the other two dropped quite exhausted beside her; and when she spun round on them, then flipped up and darted away into a puddle too small for company, neither drake followed. They sat where they were, watching her closely, jealously eyeing each other, unable to sleep though every fiber in them called out painfully for rest.

Early next day, both drakes hurried across the patch of mud to the tiny pool where the duck tranquilly floated. They were not able to get into the water—there was room only for one. They were in a quandary, for their courtship display was not natural to them on land. They hustled each other, stared at the object of their pursuit, and glanced startled up and about at other birds courting in the air and on the rapidly extending waters of the lake.

As if weary of them, the little duck rushed up into the air and flew at the swiftest pace of which she was physically capable along the marshland expanse. Both drakes pursued, extending to the limit their power of flight. The tremendous rush of air over eyes, heads, and bodies in that mile-a-minute dash, and the sense of driving every muscle to its utmost stretch, brought to them all an exhilaration near to madness. Their blood drummed hotter; their senses, strength, and confidence expanded. The white drake began to pursue closely, imperative in mien and passionate in power. As if released from a spell by his ardor, the duck broke off her arrowlike flight and dived like a stone, the others following, as if all three had been shot. When within a few feet of the ground, she turned upward at such a pace that her thrashing wings almost hummed. The pintail drake tried to flick her with his wings as she rose past his downward stoop, and the very tips of a few feathers actually brushed her back—an almost incredible maneuver, since an inch in distance or a tenth of a second in time might have blinded her or else broken his wing. She fled up the sky as if unconscious of his touch, but all her body was tremoring with it.

Now it was that the slimmer and more arrowy build of the pintail drake showed in his favor. He alone was able to copy with instant precision the insanely daring and beautiful aerobatics of the little duck as he played follow-the-leader with her up and down the sky, round treetops, sped a few inches above grasses that wavered behind them with the disturbance of their passing, skated over woods or almost scarred the silver water with the feathered keel of his breast. The mallard looked clumsy beside those two, yet he followed, thrusting along with his greater weight and strength, taking deathly risks of cornercutting that always just succeeded, coming hard beside them, once or twice turning and meeting the little duck almost head-on as she wheeled. Then she would lip up over him with her drake behind her, so close that the wind of their going would have unbalanced a weaker flier, and he would turn as if he had struck some solid thing in air, and overtake them again.

The pintail drake once or twice uttered as he flew a peculiar rolling cry, almost a sort of hissing growl, and once she replied to it on exactly the same note. The chain-lightning speed of the display was bewildering; it covered miles of country as well as miles of up-and-down zigzagging; despite the enormous speed at which they had started, they went faster and faster as if they had gone mad in the air.

The mid-air tarantella grew wilder every moment. The duck suddenly put her head back against her shoulders and began to climb perpendicularly. She went up and up—it seemed rather from some explosion of emotional force in her own body than by her throbbing wingbeats—perhaps fifty or sixty feet—then leaned over on one wing as if she had broken her heart with the effort and was about to fall. As she did so, the pintail drake, climbing behind her on a slightly slanting line, again clashed his wing tips lightly on her body, this time reaching up with them under her so that they flicked her breast. Two feet below, the white drake climbed sturdily, and as she bolted past, he attempted to duplicate the maneuver, but with a flash aside she avoided his rush.

As the pintail drake turned over to chase her down, for the first time clearly she responded to him, twisting almost faster than thought beneath him and clashing her wings under and onto his with a noise like a street rattle. At the instant of this contact, half a mile up in air, her feathered back brushed along the feathers of his breast; both were moving faster than a hundred feet a second, and any misjudgment, however fractional, meant death for them both. But the touch was a soft caress—and she was gone.

Driving round fiercely, the white drake flew deliberately at his rival as the pair parted from that flashing embrace; only the pintail's magnificent quickness saved him from a collision that would have broken the wings of both male birds. As if in sport, he zipped up and went within six inches of the white drake, over him and on after the little duck.

Down she went, nearly onto the ground, then began to flee along over the hummocky marshland, skimming it, following a course so twisty that only the eye of a bird could follow it. Her chosen drake imitated each turn and evolution, but the mallard, tiring now after more than half an hour of such flying as he had never even seen before, plowed doggedly along as straight as he could a few feet in their rear. Now, at last, she began to show her preference cruelly. She zoomed up and back before the pintail drake could turn, deliberately enticed the white drake to climb by going near enough to be touched if only he had retained the strength to do it, forced him into a heartbreaking effort, then swept about and again clashed her wings under those of the climbing pintail drake. She made the mallard attempt hopeless evolutions, underlined his weary clumsiness with her bulletlike speed, and then wing-kissed his rival not a yard from his starting eyes.

It was as if she desired to humiliate and overwhelm him, to drive him from the chase. Flashing under her own drake and bringing him like a magnet round in her pursuit, she made the mallard almost fall out of the air in avoiding them both. The more he tired, the nearer she flirted to him, the more sudden and convulsive the efforts she tempted him to make by offering herself within his reach.

Finally, she started another of those extraordinary vertical climbs. The pintail drake followed almost as steeply. But the white mallard could not do it. He could not even try. With a sullen, beaten look, he turned blindly away and glided straight down onto the swamp, landing with a clumsy splash as if his efforts had burst his heart.

At the top of their jump upward, as the duck and the drake turned together in the sky, both saw, far below, the white mallard lying motionless on the water—only now, at his side, touching him, was the dark pintail duck who had been with him before.

The pair on the wing turned along the swamp, flying over and under each other, twining miraculously and with a lovely intimacy and trust. They gamboled on a long downward slant, darted closely together onto a secret bush-ringed pool where they were private and alone, flicked into the water with their winged shoulders touching, and then in a moment the duck ceased to be the leader and surrendered to the master of her choice all that wild beauty and desire could give.

13. Family

As THE SURFACE of the ground thawed during day after day of
endless hot sunshine, it was pitted with pockets of water which
had never drained off in a million years. Patches of slender
white birch trees sprang gracefully from the earth. A covering
of spongy moss, sometimes two feet thick, covered hidden
submerged ponds. In places, hummocks of earth had been
thrown up by the winter's mighty frosts and distorted into fantastic shapes. Sharp-pronged thorny bushes thrust through the
moss and broke into a green more vivid than that ever seen
in climates soiled, however distantly, by city smokes. Gray
mud and slime sucked and gurgled here and there among the
mosses, deep and dangerous as quicksands. Sometimes, the
masses of moss grew ten or fifteen feet high in extraordinary
forms. On the right side of the swamp, there rose some hills
out of which muddy and icy streams rushed to join the big
river that wound through the middle of the marshland. And
over everything, whining gray clouds of mosquitoes, as large
as the sky clouds through which the wild ducks were accustomed to fly, rolled to and fro looking for something living
into which to sink their piercing beaks.

The pintail pair anxiously surveyed this scene as they flew

about twenty feet above it, while the duck searched for a site for their nest. The mosquitoes did not trouble them. Indeed, since arrival they had been feeding themselves fat on mosquito larvae, a delicacy which was one of the thousand joys of reaching this northland home.

Beneath them as they circled and searched, they saw hundreds of other nests, some only just begun with a few grasses laid anyhow in holes in the ground, some already containing eggs that were partly covered with down. The whole place was alive with birds. Great numbers were paired, in many cases both busily engaged parading near the chosen home, in others flying rapidly looking for likely sites, while the water of the lake and the sky about them stirred ceaselessly with couples in one stage or another of courtship display and posturing. Natural love-making is not furtive or selfish but universal; it is a part of the wholesale flowering of Spring, a culmination of communal joyfulness whose emotion grows the faster the more it is spread abroad.

Several times, the two pintails skimmed low over what looked like a perfect place to found a family. Yet that one place had been left quite untouched in this happy search by the winged thousands because there was danger there. It was a clump of tall grass high up on the side of a hummock whose top soared above and overhung it, perhaps fifty feet from the general floor of the marsh. At the hummock's base, a pretty reach of open water was patched with sprouting lily plants not yet in flower.

The little gray duck suddenly swooped swiftly down and alighted on the shelf, her mate close behind her. It was a long shelf, about twenty feet above the water, perhaps two feet wide and with a steep incline into the deep crystal of the lake.

The other sides were vertical, and even this front side would be difficult for any four-footed killer to climb, supposing he were determined enough to swim round to that side of the base. Here, it would feel safe to sit on eggs, without listening forever for the furtive tread of hairy feet in the night.

Yet both birds knew that there was something terrible about the place. The earth under their webbed feet did not feel safe. Long grass was growing there that would make perfect cover for a nest, and the buds among it showed that it would soon star with flowers that would camouflage a sitting duck's head. Everything seemed perfect except that it did not feel safe. The pair jumped off the shelf into the air, and once more they began to circle, the duck looking for something more comforting and secure.

They ranged for miles up the river valley, so far that presently they reached an area where hardly any wild ducks were to be seen, and they came upon the first nests of the geese. Then they turned, for it was useless to trespass on the goose flats where those passing millions they had seen now almost covered the ground. The drake, though playing a secondary part now, watched sharply for any place to which they might fly at the decision of his companion. His dark eyes scrutinized the base of each patch of willows or birches, the drier rushy grass, the tangled areas of bushes. Each place that appealed to her, however, they found on closer examination was already seized, for either a bird was working there and a nest had been begun, or perhaps a fussy duck stood on guard simply to indicate future intentions.

When the flying drake realized that his mate was purposefully making her way toward the ledge again, he experienced a sensation of fear. Yet he was now irrevocably committed;

he could not abandon her, nor could he sway her final decision; if she chose a place of death, he must follow. They alighted on the ledge, and without wasting more time, she shoved her way deep into the grasses that waved higher than their heads. The place was lovely even if it was sinister. The warmth of a strong sun seemed to focus here, bringing out the colors of the earth and vegetation and the austere smell of basic marsh. The water below was as deeply blue as the sky above. There was a sense of peace and security here such as could never be on level ground where most of the rest were nesting. The faint warning of danger thrilled out of the ground underfoot. It did not feel securely rooted to the side of the hummock. Somewhere in the upraised mass of earth there was a crack that gave it a different and peculiar reaction to passing winds, just as a cracked basin, if struck, sounds different from a whole one.

The drake fussed after his mate as she plunged through the tall grasses to a saucer-shaped depression at the back of the shelf. She turned, stared at him from her shining brown eyes, and then deliberately stooped and tossed some earth out of that little hollow. This was the place.

With the unquestioning docility of a natural creature, the drake abandoned his fears, turned, and flew back the way he had come. In his searchings of the morning, he had noted every place where loose edges of moss or bent bits of dead grass could be collected, and now he watched his mate work gathering them up. Arriving back with a beak full of grasses, she dug out a hollow a few inches deep and then impatiently waited. Later she began to lay the grasses in place while he watched her.

That was a blissful day. While the mosquitoes hummed, and

the wind sighed gently across the marsh and clashed the grasses and swung the willow twigs, while in the distant river great fish leaped and played, and while the air was murmuring with the wings of other wild ducks joyously content in the busy affairs of nesting or racing to and fro in mating flights, the nest on the ledge was almost completed.

On her second flight for materials, the duck saw, in the bottom of a clump of willows where rank grass grew, the white mallard with the dark duck engaged also in nest building. Anger and rivalry stirred in her a little, but she forgot these emotions as she worked. Just before feeding time at dusk, both the pintails went off together to a place where she could obtain some softer moss for lining the nest.

When they returned, she dropped her burden, stared, and suddenly uttered a fierce, low quack. For the nest she had built so carefully had been dragged to pieces, and much of its selected dry grass had vanished. With a twist and a swoop, she was off the ledge and on the wing, yet quickly as she went, the drake was before her. Some wild intuition guided him. Diving, he landed beside the white mallard's nest. The big white drake stood there belligerent while the dark duck, unheeding, went on building the stolen grasses into her own nest.

In such quandaries, there is an unwritten law of bird life. To seek a fight on the site of another's nest is to antagonize all the flock, who might combine to help drive the invader not merely away from that spot but out of the communtiy alto- gether. As the white mallard strode bristling forward, the pintail drake walked rapidly away, and his mate, observing, landed in the reeds ten yards distant. He joined her there, and they scuttled away together, completely hidden from outside, till they had found an opening in the reeds some distance away through which they could watch the white drake's nest. The two sank to the ground and remained silent. The sun was swiftly setting. Then, just as they had done, the white mallard and his mate set off flying along the marsh.

Instantly they were gone, the two pintails ran to the deserted nest. The duck picked out only her own grasses, recognizing them from the rest. She flew off. One or two were left, and these the drake pulled out and put on one side. Suddenly plowing his beak through the nest, he tossed and butted it into confusion and flung earth over it. Then, after an angry look round, he too fled.

That night, after feeding in the lake, he and his mate sat in the warm stillness of the grass on the ledge. He had forgotten the threat in the ground—at least, he only recalled it faintly sometimes. When the sun rose, he went down to wash and drink, but she did not follow him as usual. He sailed about, feeding on the juicy shoots of water plants, catching a swimming beetle, watching thousands of others doing the same. Still she did not come. Vaguely uneasy, he flew back to the ledge and pushed his way through the grasses that already had the air of welcoming him with their familiarity of shape and angle.

She was gone. Staring round, startled, he saw her, wheeling high in the sky. Something made him turn, and he saw the nest he had watched her make. It contained a single large greenish egg, and over the egg were half a dozen tiny feathers of down, each white feather branded with gray-brown and with a white tip. She had pulled them from her breast, the first part of the warm bed in which the eggs were to rest.

He looked up again and saw her pursued in flight by a

vagrant pintail drake. With a hiss of anger, he jumped straight into the air and fled to where she was playing and wheeling, and he cut so close in front of the other drake that each could feel the rush of air from the other's going. In a moment, the duck had set off wildly zigzagging, with him in pursuit, and from the first she flew so as to throw off the other wooer.

The days passed, and the Arctic summer heightened its warmth and beauty. The lake was spangled with flowers now, and there were heavy masses of white lilies floating everywhere, while the bushes and trees had taken vivid green leaf. Each day was more sunny and blue than the last. The land had forgotten its iron wintertime; now it was utterly peaceful and beautiful. There seemed to be no time there, only a dreamy succession of perfect Summer days, which grew longer and longer till presently the light never left the marsh, for the sun did not properly set.

In the nest, the number of eggs grew till at last there were nine, warmly covered with a thick coating of down above and below, and with leaves and grasses strewn over that. The mated pair spent some of every day together far from the nest, hunting for tidbits to eat, exploring the familiar land, playing in the air, or idling among the water lilies on the blueness of the lake.

The white mallard had not taken any punitive action for his plowed-up nest. He watched his mate submissively rebuild it, knowing that the community of birds would drive them out if they attempted to continue the war. In their nest, too, was a clutch of greenish eggs.

At this time, most of the birds spent long periods sailing in hundreds together about the lake. Ashore there were succulent berries and other tempting food, but there were also dangerous killers—foxes, lynxes, minks, wolverines, some of them capable of swimming in pursuit. Quite often, a duck was caught and killed, either venturing ashore or when feeding at the shallow edges of the lake.

Many fish, big and little, flittered about the lake or in the big river that bisected the marsh. The pintail drake spent an idle afternoon watching a tremendous salmon in the clear water below him, one day when he was out on the river. Its jaws beneath its big hooked nose were black and silver, its eyes sunken, its fins very big and strong, and all along one of its sides stood out in relief the old white scars where a bear's claws had struck at and just failed to grip it.

The duck was sitting tight on the eggs now. She had begun to do so when her clutch of nine eggs was complete, and the drake found himself abandoned except when he chose to go and sit on the ledge near her. She would not let him come too near the nest, and when she fled off the eggs at morning and evening for the briefest few minutes to drink and cram in a little food, she would never leave the place until he was already in the air and always flew back without him.

At first, he wandered disconsolately about the marsh, seeing thousands of other ducks sitting on their nests, too, and thousands of other drakes uneasily engaged like himself. Then he took up a position on the lake directly before his nest, where he could look up and see the ledge, though the grass hid his mate. It was at this time that the white mallard tried to establish a sort of bachelor friendship with him, coming up day after day, sailing close, dabbling sometimes, even calling attention in a friendly way to small swimming insects in the water. He had abandoned his mate and nest and lost all care for them. But the pintail drake showed no interest in him at all.

Twenty-three days after the duck had begun to sit, the pintail drake flew up nervously onto the ledge because he had seen no movement from there either the previous night at feeding time or during that morning. He had been watching anxiously, preferring not to go to the ledge, since he had been rather hostilely received there previously, but at last some obscure fear forced him to go up. He drove through the summer-yellowed grasses.

The duck was standing off the nest, looking at it, and as he came, she lifted her head and stared at him, not angrily this time but curiously. He immediately saw that two of the eggs were broken, and where they had been were two grayish and tiny balls of down, swelling and contracting as they breathed. They were alive, and he grew excited, but his effort to get nearer was defeated as she inserted her body between. He saw her lean over, and at the same time he heard the faintest pecking sound from one of the eggs. She tapped it hard once with her beak and it broke across. Out of the crack appeared a beak, a rudimentary downy face—then with a shockingly sudden and strong motion, the gray thing crashed its way out into life and air and the shell fell apart into pieces.

Afraid to anger his mate by going nearer, unable to keep still, the drake ran to the edge of the grass. As he did so, he distinctly felt the ground under his feet shiver and heard a frightened, loud *quack* from his mate, who, however, did not appear. Then the morning was as it had been, blue and beautiful, and everything seemed safe as before.

But it was not safe. Nature is never safe. As he peered out

across the expanse of the flower-spangled marsh, he saw the
wild ducks on the water scurrying for shelter among the
birches, the alders, anything—and majestically sailing overhead passed a big eagle, whose shadow fell on the lake. It
dropped suddenly, there was a scuffle and a cry, and it was
going up again, a duck held dead in its talons, and a few
feathers slowly turning and drifting down toward the water.

And again, under his feet, the drake felt that queer quiver
in the earth.

He stood there rigid, the helpless prey of conflicting desires
—to escape into the air and to stay and observe his mate and
the tiny squabs of down whose sight had moved him so sharply.
There was a sudden dreadful roaring and tumbling, the
quivering earth trembled abruptly and stopped—the drake
was on the wing in terror, under him he saw through a cloud
of dust that half the big hummock had sliced away and fallen
into the marsh. He no more dared descend than if that dust
had been smoking breath from a dragon's mouth, but he
peered down in wild alarm as he circled a few feet above.

14. The Fire

THE DUST from the landslip, caused by the lake water's eating its way under one side of the big hummock, swirled heavily around, and for a minute or two, the drake, despite his dartings, could not see the extent of the damage. Then, at last, he saw a raw black edge where the end of the ledge had been. A turn of the smoky dust showed him that, although two-thirds of the ledge had dropped into the lake, the piece on which the nest rested was still in place; his mate's instinct to build there had not been wrong.

In a moment, he was down among the grasses again, yet haunted by a horror that another fall might occur. However, the ground felt solid now—more solid than it had ever done. He shoved through and found the duck, apparently unaware of the cataclysm, breaking another eggshell. Some sort of joy and triumph mixed in him, and he winged off the ledge again and flew the whole length of the valley, out over the goose flats where the ground crawled with birds, and spent the whole morning playing on the wing.

The fleeting shadow of a cloud rushed up the river course and over the marsh, and in a second the drake was racing it, fleeing along with head and tail outstretched, and had gone

five miles almost before he knew he had turned. As that enter-
tainment ended, he noticed three swans in labored flight,
their long necks rigid, low over a marshy extension of the
lake, and he zipped dangerously close under them, past and
away. All three jerked their heads round after him as if they
had been parts of a single bird and gave him an indignant,
hostile stare. As he vanished, he heard one of them call, a
glorious bell-like tone, deep and golden, echoing through the
air for miles.

Over a broad pond shining white with lilies, he saw a fly
on the wing and turned and caught it in mid-air and swallowed
it hastily. He dropped to the ground in a patch of bushes, the
fly having aroused his never-sleeping appetite. He pecked at
and turned over a mushroom but was not impressed with its
flavor. Then he set himself to enjoy a comprehensive snack
consisting of blueberries and mossberries, which in glorious
size and profusion almost covered the place where he was.
Like all wild ducks, he was partial to the juicy Arctic berries
—strawberries, cranberries, salmonberries, bearberries, anything he could find.

He stood among the low-growing bushes, enjoying their
shapes and examining with a bird's intense vision every graceful curve and color mass in the luxuriant foliage. He flew up,
sated, and went slowly along the big river. At a point where
the banks were deep-cut by the current and where the long
spell of sunny days had caused the level to fall unusually low,
he swooped down and landed. From the clay of the bank on
one side projected enormous bones of prehistoric mastodons,
pale and pitted. The place stank, but the drake did not mind
that. He knew that, in such an ancient boneyard as this, fat
flies came to breed; and after the berries, his palate ached for

tender meat. He searched to and fro industriously, found a little heap of slowly curling weevils, eyed them gluttonously for a minute without moving, then struck at them and swallowed the lot.

A sudden memory of those newly hatched squabs of down in the nest sent him soaring, and he turned with instinctive accuracy directly for it and flew racing back. It was late in the day, and some of the other ducks were out feeding now, but his mate was there, sitting warmly on the nest. She stayed where she was when he pushed his way up to her, and this time there was no hostility nor any sign that he must keep away. After a few minutes, she got up, and there in the nest were nine of those queer little creatures, their bodies swelling and shrinking as they breathed, their eyes not now open. Their down, now he could examine it, was still wet from their confinement in the egg; a tiny scrap of shell adhered to one of them.

As he stood over them, one stirred, and its beak silently opened and remained open, a yellow and gaping void waiting for food. Immediately, every impulse in him thrilled with the selfish desire for something to eat. He looked about, plunged through the tall yellow grass, leaped off the new razor edge of the ledge, and planed down to a particular corner of the lake where there was always plenty of mosquito larvae. Returning after taking his fill of them, he found things exactly as he had left them—his mate standing watching, the one greedy youngster still with its mouth wide. Nervously, with an eye on his mate in case she struck at him, he moved a little closer to watch the new live thing. It jerked queerly. In alarm, he flopped down to get some more food for himself.

His mate had gone when he returned. He took another look at his offspring. As he turned to go, the duck came back from

hastily feeding. And from then on, she was going to and fro
ceaselessly, seeking soft insect food and aquatic stuff for herself. Anxiety allowed her only a hurried snatching of a few
mouthfuls between journeys.

The drake tired of it. He wanted to watch the little ones, but
he wanted still more to feed himself, and the night was his
natural time for eating seriously. He went down onto the lake
presently and found the white mallard gorging on a wriggling
cloud of swimming leeches he had spotted in a shallow. The
pintail assisted notably, and for once the white drake was not
resentful. He even sat watching, toward the end, perhaps as a
gesture of friendship, though quite possibly because he was
not able to eat any more himself.

Once during the night, the pintail drake went back to his
family. The duck was sitting with them under her breast,
keeping them warm. He stayed there for a time, vaguely pro-
prietary, but after a time it seemed to him that there might be
more leeches in the lake, and he went back to see.

All next day, the tiny ducks remained in the nest, being
watched mainly by their mother and erratically by the drake,
who began to find them a nuisance and felt more and more
inclined to spend his day hours with the white mallard and
other drakes who were sleeping and lazing on the water.

Some time later on, however, when he went to the nest in
the morning, he found the little duck gently propelling with
her bill one of the fledglings toward the cliff edge, where the
shelf had broken away. When the nest was built, there was a
steep but easily walkable slope down to the water, but the land-
slide had cut it off vertically. In alarm, the drake whistled
loudly, but his mate took not the least notice of this ineffectual
masculine outcry. She nosed the tiny, jerky thing to the ex-

treme edge, and it looked over, stood transfixed with interest,
then scurried round its mother's feet back into the grass. In
turn, she brought them all out for their first look at the great
world. They were all quite active now and had made many
adventurous journeys of exploration through the grasses that
were so much taller than themselves, but always hitherto they
had flinched back from the glare of daylight outside.

Next morning, when the maneuver was being repeated, the
drake stood looking on with a sort of casual pride. Then, without the least warning, the duck got her bill under the first
nestling and tipped it over the edge. It vanished, and as the
drake craned terrified to watch, he saw it roll down the side of
the hummock and hit the lake water with a small splash. Then
he saw that it was floating, afraid to move, rigid, but certainly
floating right side up. In a moment, he had jumped down and
settled on the water beside it. Then he did not know what to
do next.

Plop! Another of them had come down, also successfully.
The first was striking out with its feet, trying to run on the
water but swimming in a spasmodic and alarmed way. Instinctively, he started to swim alongside it, but it paid him no
attention. It reached the base of the hummock, glanced up
wildly, then sat there unable to move. The second nestling
splashed up and joined it.

Seven of them came down in that abrupt and dangerous
manner, all quite safely. They squattered into a tight group
at the bottom of the hummock, the nearest they could get
to their lost home, and waited, too frightened to stir, and
still more frightened by the well-meant attempts of the drake
to attract them by swimming near. To them, he was enormous,

alarming, and a stranger. He felt afraid himself from their
fear.

Perhaps the duck thought the remaining two too small for
the drop. Perhaps she knew their wings and legs were not
strong enough. At least, she had other plans for them. She
brought one to the edge, squatted low beside it, and by a
clever flick of one wing, scuffed it up onto her back between
her pinions. Before it could move off, she flew forward over
the lake, slowly and quietly, stretched her wings, glided down
toward the water, and then suddenly checked her descent a
foot above the surface, dropped her tail, and the nestling slid
gently off into the water as its mother touched down on the
lake a couple of feet ahead. She swam round to where the
others were, the tiny one almost running along the surface
in his frantic haste to follow. Eight little ducks, huddled
together, clung near the base of the cliff now. Their father was
ignored and sat watching them, perplexed; these methods of
treating small things were altogether too much for him.

One remaining nestling, uttering minute and feeble cries,
ran about on the edge of the shelf above. The duck flew up
to it, stooped over and touched it comfortingly, then flicked it
negligently onto her back like the other, and flew down,
discharging it over her tail onto the water as before.

While the tiny creature was righting itself on the water,
before its mother could turn, there was a rush and a great
ripple, a splash—and an old pike had snapped the fledgling
and swum away with it under the water. The pintail duck's
head struck with a snakelike hiss, and her hard bill went
within half an inch of the great fish's eye, which stared at
her as, jerking its tail and fins, it skidded aside. The savage

blow hit its scaly head and raked along its fifty-pound muscular body. Had the blow been a fraction nearer, the pike would have been blinded, but even then it would never have let go of its prey. Hundreds of baby ducks die this way every summer; from their birth, enemies cluster about them on every side, on land, in the water, and in the air.

The little duck came round again like a flash and uselessly dived after the pike. She came up again a minute later, in a terrified flurry to protect the rest of her brood; the little ones still huddled quietly at the base of the cliff from whose safety they had so suddenly been flung into a cruel world.

She led them, and they followed, toward a shallow, and just as fast as their jerky little feet could propel them, they got to the shore and scrambled awkwardly and thankfully up onto the mud. They had had their first swimming lesson and wanted no more. They began to explore, nervously, with agitated runs back to their mother whenever a grass moved strangely or a shadow intercepted their way. She taught them to eat mosquito larvae and showed them how to search for the food on their own. One or two took an interest; the others preferred to explore or wandered about examining and falling over things. They did not return to the water that day.

Next morning, she showed them what to do if any real danger threatened on land. She gathered them to her with soft whispering cries, spread her wings over them, then leaped into the air, leaving them there rigidly holding the positions they had had when under her wings. They looked very odd, some erect, some crouching, some huddled hard together, but they did not move. She soared, watched them closely, then returned. She was pleased with them, and let them feed awhile. After that, she put them through the practice a score of times, until they automatically remained motionless every time she raised her wings.

Then came another lesson—how to escape from perils. Instead of flying, she lifted her wings high, then ran off and left them. She began to circle round, quacking miserably and going jerkily as if wounded. The first time, they tried to run to her, and she flew back angrily and beat them sharply with her wings. Then away and round again. This time, they stayed where they were. Once more, the trick was practiced over and over again. When they had done it half a dozen times, she stopped abruptly in the midst of shamming wounded and called to them. They began to run toward her, whereat she called again in a sharper note, and at that they fell in a rigid group once more while she circled and fluttered. So she taught them always to run at one note, always to freeze into immobility at another. In this way, while pretending to be hurt and escaping so as to lead away pursuit, she could direct them when to run, when to stop, and in which direction to go. It was a game, like most human and animal games of the wild, with a deadly purpose to it. And they learned it well.

At night, now, since they could not regain the nest on the ledge, all sheltered together under the roots of some bushes. After a day or two, she took them onto the water again. There, more teaching games commenced. She would dip deep below the surface, come up with a tip of juicy pondweed, and throw it among them. The quickest would seize it but, being too small to be able to bolt it, would attempt to swim away, the others chasing. First one, then another would get hold of it. It showed them how to maneuver on water; they lost their stiff uneasiness and swam naturally; soon, they, too, were trying to dip for food, sometimes upsetting themselves and rolling about, tiny balls of grayish-brown almost as light as thistledown.

All over the lake, by this time, there were low mellow cries from mothers teaching their nestlings and the mouselike squeaks of the tiny things excitedly answering. They learned to catch small insects, aquatic flies, and mosquitoes for themselves and dashed about after them, using enormous energy. They snapped up water seeds. Their greatest desire was to imitate their parents in catching flies, either on the wing or alighted on blades of grass or reed. This, however, they were not strong and quick enough to do until they were older, but they spent stupendous efforts and incredible cunning on the study. To see one of them stalking a fly, by land or water, was a study in natural swiftness, intentness, and savagery. The fly would wait till the last second, till the little feathered head was actually striking forward with open bill, then flip sideways, up and down onto another—or even the same—bit of grass.

The pintail duck caught flies and flung them down, crawling and half-stunned, into the water or on the ground, to watch her offspring grab them up. It was also a pastime of hers to catch a dragonfly, grasshopper, or locust and fling it into the water hard, uninjured but soaked so that it could whizz about, shooting to and fro at high speed and odd angles, but unable to rise. The whole flock of little ones would then run along the surface in chase, their eagerness, greed, and lightness enabling them apparently to flicker over the water with their feet on top of it.

Once or twice, pintail mothers would fly carrying their nestlings to the water, though rarely, and tilt them in from the air. The tiny things would float down with little wings and feet spread out and drop into the water, safe and right side up. The days passed golden with sunshine. The blue changeless skies reflected in the blue of the lake. More and more flowers came out. At night, from their shelter under the bush, the little family watched the rabbits playing in the moonlight and dancing home before dawn; they never showed during the day. The ducks also heard wolves howling at night, far away in the hills.

The pintail drake became less and less inclined for the company of his offspring and even of his mate. Sometimes he would swim near her, the eight little ones making a string behind them, and their course would be intersected by scores of other families out for an airing. Sometimes he saw the dark duck with ten fledglings obediently at her tail, but the white mallard was never with her now. Often, the drake saw him at night, and he was more friendly than ever. Indeed, scores of the drakes were now accustomed to congregate together for sleep or to feed, away from the ducks and the small birds.

It was one Summer night, when he was idly feeding among a big concourse of other drakes far down the lake, that he saw the fire. Very far away, in silence, the sky began to redden faintly, and all the birds in alarm knew that this terrible color was not moonlight or any other natural thing. They watched it stiff-necked as it glowed brighter and seemed to come nearer, spreading from a tiny patch to a bluish-red flush that gradually stained half the night sky.

Before any sound or other evidence of trouble reached them, the nervous and restless ducks could smell the first faint tinges of smoke. By this time, the trees and hummocks about the marsh were red-stained on one side as the menacing light reflected from the sky. It was from the direction of the forest that the fire was approaching, and it was coming at the speed of a galloping horse, but still, out in the marsh where the ducks were, nothing of the conflagration could be heard.

The birds stiffened, and all turned together. A red fox was running slinkily out from the trees. He came on across the swamp, round the edge of the lake, and the birds crowded away to the middle. For a moment, the pintail drake thought of his mate and her young under the bush. But the fox had more urgent things to think of. He ran on steadily and vanished in the direction of the goose flats.

A minute later, a pair of spotted lynxes trotted into view, their eyes glimmering redly as they ran. They went through the reeds, turning neither to left nor right, after the fox. Then came a wolverine, blackish-brown and furry, with a dead rabbit in its jaws. It, too, was fleeing, and it ran swiftly on out of sight.

The creatures were running from the fire that could now just be heard as a sort of murmuring whisper far away in the spruce forest. They wanted to put the open, wet space of the marsh behind them; the fire could not jump that. Flickers of flame reflection that seemed to run half across the sky were now leaping beyond the area of red on the clouds. A sudden crash of falling timber, probably two or three big trees together, spat sparks over the treetops, and the general noise of burning rose to a muffled roar.

The ducks, redly illuminated, did not fly, but kept together well out on the lake. They were safe there, but horribly frightened by the panic that fire arouses among all wild things. An elk appeared utterly silently, stepping from the woods and pausing. The fire glowed on his huge palmate antlers and ungainly body. Suddenly, he set off across the swamp, choosing the harder places, his pace that of a good horse. Away he went, remarkably silent except for an occasional squelch underfoot, and disappeared after the rest toward the goose flats.

Suddenly, the ground became alive with running creatures of all sizes in a fleeing mob. There were muskrats, a lone wolf, rabbits, a mink, a pair of foxes, and finally a big reindeer, his antlers rising and falling as he galloped, his brown body gleaming in the firelight glow. He rattled along, and the last the ducks saw of him was his white-patched hindquarters disappearing after the rest of the fugitives. Among those fleeing things were many beasts of prey and many of their natural victims. At any ordinary time, the killers would have hunted and the others fled for their lives. For this night, before the scorching breath of a greater killer, the ancient feuds were forgotten, and fox and rabbit ran almost shoulder to shoulder with lynx and hare.

After the reindeer had gone, the fire seemed to take a frightful and enormous leap forward. It suddenly appeared, climbing and swirling about among the distant trees. It turned them scarlet and black. They began to bend and curl, with grotesque and horrid cracking noises. A hundred simultaneously exploded like tall bombs, flames blowing wildly outward. With a blast that was deafening and enveloping, the main body of the fire poured like a red ocean through the shriveling forest and thumped down on the open marsh, sending steam from the pools bursting sky-high among clouds of wood cinders, ashes, and leaping and scattering sparks.

The wild ducks on the water cowered and bent their heads.

15. Eclipse

THE INSTINCT to stay on the lake was based on a wild consciousness that there they were safest and also on a compulsion not to leave their mates and half-winged families. These little ones could not yet fly, and the mother birds would rather burn alive than desert them; after such forest fires, wild ducks have been found sitting dying on their nests, their burned bodies having quite protected their nestlings under them. Out on the lake itself, the drakes were away from risk, since the marsh was too wide and wet for even that racing conflagration to jump it. Not all the ducks or nestlings were so fortunate. Some had made their homes as far as a mile from the water.

After the fire had gone crackling and roaring away up and down the river, the drakes, at first in ones and twos, presently in a mob, took wing and began to search the cindery desolation in a vague alarm. Great clouds of smoke rose sullenly where the woods had been. Charred and blackened stumps stuck out of the ground, whose very leaf mold had caught fire, and now glowed and darkened as though the earth itself had become a stupendous dragon with heaving sides transparently giving reflections from its molten belly. Here and there, a tree trunk that had somehow escaped the worst of the blaze suddenly

132

cracked into flames, spouted sparks and color, and then died to black writhings.

The pintail drake raced in and out of the smoke clouds, only twenty feet or so from the hot and stifling ground, looking along the edge of the lake at the chaos. He saw other ducks crawling on burnt feet through the ashes, their protesting little ones hobbling after them, seeking bits of ground that had not been badly burned, so that their progress wavered to and fro and sometimes traced rough circles. Where a drake identified his mate, he would swoop down and try to alight, kicking hot dust into the night air and winging away again, leading her anxiously toward the safety of the lake. Scores of the birds, old and young, died that night, either in the fire or afterward. Up on the goose flats, the slaughter was ten times more dreadful.

At last, the drake saw his duck. She was on the water, a short distance out from the lake's edge, with her brood packed terrified behind her. All were safe. He had almost lost interest in her, but this dreadful night brought it back. He sheered down on the water at her side, and they cowered together, the hot breaths of smoky wind coming chokingly offshore from where the stumps and ruin glowed less frequently now. The duck had led her family at a run out of their night shelter on land when the first whiffs of smoke reached it. They had just had time to swim madly out twenty yards before the flames struck down on the marsh edge. The little duck's back was very faintly singed, and every time he smelt it, the drake ruffled away in terror and disgust.

By this time, almost all the survivors, young and adult, were on the lake, which had never been so crowded with life before. The original thousands who had migrated here had

been multiplied by about seven, and the whole lake surface
was covered by a faintly moving glimmer of feathered bodies
riding the ripples as far as the eye could see. It was the first
time they had all been together, and when dawn came, each
duck with her convoy of youngsters stared and craned, clucked
and spread out protecting or reproving wings.

The fire was almost a tragedy in another way for these
thousands of birds. Previously, they had gathered a good deal
of their food by digging succulent small creatures out from
under the rich loam of the forest. The fire had killed or
scared away all these. Now, the lake itself had to provide
everything for them all. That blast of fire striking the water
and the marsh had even destroyed innumerable billions of mosquitoes and mosquito larvae, but the northland was able to
fill that gap, huge new clouds of the insects drifting in at once
to fill the vacated space, just as the air might fill a temporary
vacuum. Indeed, the mosquito invasion was so dense that,
for a day or two after the fire, the sky was at times obliterated
over large areas, as by drifts of fog.

The young birds at this time became completely familiar
with the water. Hitherto they had enjoyed hunting on it or
sitting dreaming on it for a short time, but to rest they had
always preferred land. Now, with something of a food short-
age, they were diving constantly, staying for long periods out
of sight under the water. The adults hardly ever dived and
looked on slightly startled or scandalized when their brood
vanished under the water, sometimes one or two at a time, but
more often twenty or thirty young birds together, greedily
following each other down to see what was available to eat
and not coming up for several minutes, finally popping out
at some different part of the lake to which they had swum

under the water. All the time, the lake was a babble of chattering, quacking, whistling, and splashing, such a playground as
worried humanity never dreams of, a place of sunshine, movement, beauty of color and action, a piece of the earth's surface
completely without worry or care or anything but natural and
innocent enjoyment of a peaceful family and communal life.

When the small birds were three weeks old, their first real
feathers had appeared on the flanks and scapulars and tail
became noticeable for the first time. A week later, feathers
were showing on rump, breast, head, and neck. They looked
strange little things, half downy, half quilled, impertinent,
everlastingly hungry, greedy enough to fight each other and
to try to steal from their parents or other adult birds, who
became increasingly abrupt with them, capable at any moment
of knocking the young things heels over head with a half-
savage blow of bill or wing. They were gray-brown, with the
crown of the head a dark clove and the sides mainly gray-white
fading to a white throat and chin, the back a clove brown
darkening on the rump, with chest and sides of the head a
pinkish buff. They were pretty, boisterous, absurd, appealing,
stalking each other with exaggerated caution through grasses
infinitely taller than themselves, standing transfixed to examine a blossom much larger than their heads, having scampering
races, attempting ridiculously to fly straight up in the air after
a passing insect, falling into the water, and there vanishing
under the surface like something sunk without trace. As they
grew a little older, their colors paled and their long pin-tail
feathers became noticeable.

At first, the young drakes and ducks were almost indistinguishable, all resembling their mothers. As they grew older,
some advanced much more rapidly toward fuller plumage

than others whose wings grew less quickly, the long flight feathers obstinately refusing to develop. Yet they all felt within their bodies a consciousness that the air was their rightful element, and they constantly made efforts to fly.

The drakes generally paid less and less attention to their mates. Some of them casually tried to rival the young things when the latter began seriously flying. The pintail drake did so again and again. A curious inner urgency drove him. At this time, his snowy breast feathers were showing a strange spottiness. Some of them began to fall out. He became agitated, pecking at the loose feathers to detach them. Yet the more he cleaned away, the more loose ones appeared, and soon feathers were loosening on his neck and head. When he flew, his wings and tail seemed thinner, less able to carry his weight. No feathers had fallen from them so far, but he existed in a state of irritability and suspicion, afraid that his flight powers were failing and constantly going to great heights and performing aerobatic feats to satisfy himself. Other drakes did the same, and the air over the lake became full of them, at times, fighting off this sense of creeping paralysis, spattering their feathers down the air, and performing amazing feats of flying in all sorts of crazy ways.

As his nervousness increased, his vague jealousy of the younger drakes became fiercer. He remembered it only at times, but then he would chase the small and playful creatures out of whatever place they were in, drive them before him with savage strokes of his bill up a low bluff over the lake's edge, and attempt to push them off. There was a twelve-foot drop to the water there. They always evaded him, at first with frightened cries, but soon with genial filial contempt. It became a game which they patiently enjoyed, and they would run right to the edge, peer over, wait till he stalked within a few inches, and leap squawking aside just as he jumped at them—sometimes so late that he almost precipitated himself over instead.

Then came a sunny morning, when they were in the midst of this game and noisily enjoying it while the drake's temper rapidly worsened. The biggest of the fledglings, a strong, saucy young drake, was balancing himself on the edge, looking down, really half eager for the jump. His father was standing a few feet away to his right, exhausted after chasing the others to and fro. Light as a shadow, the little duck sailed low over the grass from behind, bumped her daring offspring before he could look round. With a cry, he half fell but half flew about ten yards and hit the water with a splash.

The others of the brood watched petrified. They did not realize that their playtime had ended also. With silent dispatch, their mother rounded them up despite their evasive rushes. One after another, they were shuffled, flapped, or bundled over the edge. It did not matter whether they went forward, backward, sideways or upside down, but they had to go, and go they did. Some flew many yards. Some fell almost vertically. Those which fell badly hit the water hard and did not like it. Those which flew well were able to settle on the lake not merely with comfort but with obvious vanity.

The duck, grimly businesslike, flew down speedily after them and began to drive them out of the water onto the shore. Those who had found flying unpleasant skidded off along the surface, crying out their fears. The others, not without protests but privately with some enjoyment, allowed themselves to be shepherded to the top again, and this time two of them jumped off of their own accord, while the others, although pushed over, flew down quite strongly. When the duck came down on the water to repeat the performance once more, all their brood except one still fluffy little drake who had always been nervous ran to the top of the bluff quite happily to try this new game again. After that, flying was their continual pastime. At first, they merely made increasingly long horizontal flights from a height a few feet over the water. Then they learned to rise from the level ground. After that, and with many ludicrous efforts ending in duckings, they found they could jump into the air off the water, though not so vertically as their parents. And finally came the fascinating pastime of getting on the wing and attempting to climb really high into that alluring blue Arctic sky.

Pure and unalloyed physical happiness is the birthright of wild creatures, and in no other way is it demonstrated so exquisitely as in learning to fly. These young birds found an ever-new world under their wings. First, the whole length of the lake, wandering and vivid blue, set in the width of the bright-green marsh that was still spangled everywhere with summer flowers. Then came flights over the foothills that hemmed in the marsh. The young birds learned the delights of woods, spiced and silent, their only sound that of the breeze wandering through the leaves. They explored the black mysterious path where the fire had come; already, all sorts of vegetation and flowers were pushing their tangled way through the ashes. The birds flew far up the river, watching the fish leap and the small animals play in the sunshine.

But most of their joy came from the feeling of wings, the sudden lightning turn in mid-air, the breathless swoop down a mile of scented breeze, the myriads of new aspects of their world obtained as they sailed and changed direction again

and again in purest delight because everything beneath them
was so endlessly beautiful.

The drake's uneasy resentment of his offspring both on
the ground and in the air he loved so wildly, marked a strange
and terrifying phase in his life. For about at this time he
found that he could fly no more. The molting that had at first
speckled and soon almost bared his breast had spread like
some chronic disease until it reached his wings and tail. The
long flight feathers on which his balance and steering de-
pended had fallen out, one or two at first, then as if the roots
of all of them together had withered. Wherever he went, he
left feathers exquisite in texture and colors but somehow woe-
fully flaccid in condition.

It was during an evening after he had watched his brood
playing in the sky that he found he could not fly. Having begun
to feed, he remembered a place where he had noticed a new
patch of berries, a mile down the river. He tried to rise off
the water and fell over ridiculously on his side. He was swimming again in a second; but now he knew, and knew finally,
that he must not attempt to fly again.

Already, except for the larger size of his deformed wings,
he was indistinguishable in color from the little duck. She
could fly; yet she, too, looked curiously thin and naked, and
her wings seemed ragged and broken-tipped. And as the weeks
passed, fewer and fewer of the wild ducks of the original
migrating company were seen in the air, which was soon
surrendered completely to the smaller, slimmer, less brightly
plumaged youngsters of that year.

A great change came over the marsh. Instead of the unending chorus of chattering, quacking, and whistling which

marked the presence of the wild-duck horde, the place became relatively silent. Formerly, great flocks of the birds could be seen resting and sleeping in the bright days, feeding and washing and preening at morning and evening, and there was plenty of sound of them dabbling, feeding, and moving about at night. Now, the young birds flew by day, but often set out on long journeys in companionable crowds; they would be away, most of them, during the greater part of each day, extending their explorations and adventures farther and farther afield and so, by a natural process, preparing themselves for their first great migration flight southward.

Meanwhile, most of the adult birds who came north in the Spring were in hiding and in misery. They had, it seemed, a great shame. They were half naked, with ragged and unequal feathers that fell out at a touch. They crept away from the lake into the long reedy grass of the swamp and found places to hide all day. They hid in mobs, mostly groups of one sex being together, though in some cases several sets of pairs sheltered as a group.

The pintail drake and his duck found themselves with half a dozen other birds in a hideaway under a thick clump of bushes, round whose roots coarse marsh grass had grown about two feet high. The ducks shoved and nosed their way into the very heart of this jungle and crouched there, bodies pressed against each other as if in an extremity of fear or disgust. The white mallard drake, who had followed the pintail drake for some time now, crept in there after him, and the dark duck with him.

In that yellowish twilight among the overhanging grass, it was stuffy, damp, muddy, and cold. The birds miserably hid themselves there from dawn to dusk. They passed the

time in a sort of irritable sleep, dreaming of flight, which now
seemed the only thing to be desired. They heard again the
rhythmic swish of thousands of wings on the long flight northward and the crash of the roller as it climbed the reef and so
nearly overwhelmed them (in their dreams, they started, stirring their wing stumps, as if to escape by flight); the pintail
drake remembered the red fox's leap and how he had fled
through the air just above that snapping monster—but wings
saved him. All the time, it was wings of which he thought—
wings, wings, wings.

At night, after dark, they would creep nervously out, stumble through the rough sedges and mud hills, and find their
way to the lake's edge. There, not going far out, they would
feed hastily among hundreds of their unfeathered kind and
would stare balefully as proud young drakes and ducks of
that Summer, almost fully fledged now, sailed among them in
plumaged beauty or winged their way up into the night sky.
Then the old birds, never looking at each other, would shuffle
back to their lairs, inadequately fed, thirsty sometimes, and
crouch down to the ground, waiting till this strange and
wretched dispensation should pass. Week after week of their
molt went by. Already, a new spirit was stirring in them.
Perhaps, with the fading of their own beauty, the glory of the
wilderness around them had lost its appeal. Or perhaps they
could feel, although there was as yet no sign, the first withering
shivers of coming Winter death. At least, the tranquil happiness of the Summer passed with the feathers that floated from
their breasts as their molt began, and uneasiness and restless
urges began once more to stir among them all.

There came a Summer night, an hour or so only, and even
then so bright with the northern reflection of the midnight

sun from just below the horizon that the clouds over them were hazily shining, when that group of molting wild birds stirred suddenly and in terror, and their involuntary movement was followed by a silent shrinking so close to the ground that they seemed to wish to become part of it.

A smell had come to them, very faint and very sour and rank. No sound at all—only the ghost of smell—but the smell spelt dreadful danger. It remained constant for a minute or two. Then it grew suddenly stronger. A stench. And then they all heard a dreadful sound. It was the sound of softly padded feet being contracted, lifted, moved through the air, and stealthily set down where the earth neither squelched nor sent rolling grains of dust, but silently received them. These birds could not fly. The muscles of their wings crawled in their backs, but they knew they could not fly. The one, the only sure way of escape, the way they would have taken at the very first suspicion of this enemy's approach, was impossible to them, and they knew it.

In their hideaway under the bush roots, they crouched, pushing even their heads hard onto the wet earth, flattening their bodies, helpless and hopeless, as if they were asking that their inevitable slaying should be done at least quickly.

The stench became unbearable as the killer—whose sense of smell was the keenest in all the wild—paused not four feet away, his furred shoulders among the bushes over their heads, his cruel jaws almost touching them, his sensitively sniffing nostrils aflare taking in their scent.

With one taloned paw, he began gently and unhurriedly moving the twigs that hid them from his green, moonlit eyes.

16. The Killer

THE CREATURE that was slowly, almost with relish, digging out the wild ducks from their hideaway was a lynx.

Not much smaller than a leopard, with long, powerful limbs and a stumpy tail, it could eat half a dozen ducks in a night, but its nature was of that savage sort that slaughtered not merely for food but for the delight of feeling blood about its jaws. It was a killer not for use but by desire. Its fur was long and soft, gray-brown with darker, handsome spots. Its ears, upright and tufted, seemed to listen for movements in the undergrowth it was carefully pulling apart. Its eyes, so intent that the pupils had narrowed to straight black lines in the glimmering green irises, gave the impression of actually seeing through the leaves and twigs and feeding themselves in advance on the contours of the crouching victims below.

Scrape—scratch—pause. In the absolute silence, for the lynx was controlling its breathing so as to listen, some bits of mud fell from the roof of the shelter onto the pintail drake's back, and he convulsively hollowed it away from the terrifying contact.

He felt paralyzed; he could not fly, and now he could not run, could not even stand. Sour and stinking, the smell of the lynx sank through the leaves and seemed to drown them in corruption. The methodical way the covering was removed suggested an obscene gentleness that had no wish to hurry the final act when their blood would spurt.

Scratch—scrape—and a thin sliver of moonlight came knife-like onto the back of the dark duck. Although it seemed that she could not physically press closer to the ground, yet at that touch she sank. And then, for what seemed an endless and formless extension of time, there was no sound, no movement above or below, only an icy coldness not belonging to the Summer night that had entered the hideaway along the moonbeam.

More delicately than before, as if with an air of soft apology, the great paw over their bent heads moved again—and the moonbeam ray opened and became a spotlight nakedly exposing them all, crouched like victims prepared for sacrifice.

Instantly, out of the silence and petrification, there came a veritable explosion of force, incarnate savagery, and released terror. As with two chain-lightning blows of taloned paws, the lynx struck, the pintail drake, his little speckled duck, and some others sprang with beating wing stumps and thrashing feet upward and outward, screaming. The back of the dark duck, the white mallard's mate, had been sliced heart deep and the head of another bird ripped clean off by those first two rakes from the killer's claws, and with the dead bodies flapping under his feet he snapped down a third victim as it raced past his head. Then the rest were away, beating and leaping over the five yards to the lake's edge and into the water, with the huge bulk of the killer jumping to overtake them.

It seemed to them that they were being pursued by something as big as a tree, something against whose springing speed they had no visible motion. A shadow over the pintail drake blotted out the night; he heard a sickening thump and the squeaking gasp as the breath of life tore through the ripped side of a fleeing bird behind him; the lynx spurned the dying thing and jumped again. The bird he had struck rolled under his foot, and that saved the white mallard's life, for the next blow, meant to cut him down, twisted and raked up the mud beside him, spattering him as he instinctively hopped sideways away from the air rush of the blow.

Then the birds were in the water and had scuttered to the deep and dived out of sight. After them, so close that his hot, panting breaths hurried them, came the lynx, hitting the water with a crash that sent spray all over them as they tipped under the surface.

The pintail drake, in a great spasm of terror, was at first scuffling along on the bottom in the dim moony gleam under the surface, but soon it was deep enough to swim with several feet of water over him. Behind, he could hear the lynx, which had picked him out to pursue, driving along through the water, swimming, looking about for him. The beast's great furry strokes enormously agitated the lake about him and sent tremors to the escaping bird.

The drake forced himself along at the very top of his physical power, his neck extended, his eyes starting, his head a little raised. He held his body under the water at an angle as if leaning forward to run. His wings were held stiff, partly open, but not used to propel himself forward, being rather employed as a sort of fin. His feet struck alternately with powerful blows as if he was running rather than swimming. He looked exactly as does a frightened chicken racing across a road, but his movements were so much slower as to be ludicrous, though horror was driving him almost to the breaking of his heart.

He was now twenty feet deep under the surface, and about a foot from the lake bottom. He swam perhaps forty feet, and there before him the bottom shelved suddenly and steeply off. He stopped, turning slowly in the water, maintaining his depth. He was looking, listening for dear life, using all his sense to discover the approach of the lynx.

There was no sound.

About him, on the edge of that underwater cliff, he could very faintly see in the drowned moonlight some lily pads and grasses slowly waving in the water with the agitation of his swimming. Then, as he listened, he heard or felt an impulse in the coldness round him that was caused by something huge and foreign swimming not far away.

Instantly, he seized a tough lily root in his bill and held on, ceasing to paddle so that no ripple should betray him. Some underwater current of the lake slowly floated his body up till his head was the lowest part, still holding on with that death-like grip to the lily root. The tremor in the water became more pronounced; the killer was coming, swimming along the surface, abandoning for the time the several dead ducks on shore in an obsession of rage and a lust to kill those who had dared to escape.

The drake heard, felt a great form sliding through the water far above him, then, as he frantically gripped hold of the root, saw the shadow shoot along the surface overhead. Back it came again, the deadly paws hauling it along, the green eyes catching a touch of moonshine as they stared with quick jerks of the head this way and that. They seemed to be obsessed with killing lust. Then the lynx had gone by again, far upon the surface.

It did not return any more, but began swimming ashore with that same feverish energy, back to the birds it had slaughtered. Having landed, it began furiously to gorge.

The drake released his hold on the lily root, which, in his terror, had been so strong that it would have needed a powerful pull to break him away from it. He began swimming again, rapidly but with failing power, back at an angle to the way he had come, still about twenty feet underwater. His legs moved in front of each other slower and slower, but he persisted with that extraordinary blind repetition that wild things can conjure up at need, and after an endless time, his head broke the surface of the lake and he was striding through the shallows. He had sense enough to seek the taller, rougher marsh grass that would hide him as he pushed his way through it. He was too exhausted even to remember the presence of the killer. He simply lurched a few paces through the grass and sank down, semiconsciously uneasy and flutteringly sensitive that some terrible thing was within almost touching distance; he could not define what it was.

He must, in his fatigue, have emerged from the lake much nearer than he intended to the point of his entry. For he suddenly heard a cracking crunch of bones and flesh, a rending and the noise of air being sucked into a stuffed mouth. The lynx was feeding, perhaps a hundred yards away, lying down and tearing apart a carcass that had been the drake's immediate neighbor in the bushy hideaway. With a pang of fear and anger, he remembered his mate. Where had she gone in that frantic flurry out of the bushes? Had she found safety among the waving weed roots of the lake bottom, clinging there in the mud-swirling dimness under the water while the killer plunged furiously by? Or was she one of the victims

over whose bleeding bones the drake could hear that rough
tongue luxuriously scraping at this moment?

Too overborne to attempt to escape again, he crouched
where he was, and if the lynx had come that way, the tired victim would have died in his tracks, unable even to reach the
water a second time. But the lynx was sated. It fed more slowly,
rested, fell to again with brutal avidity, stopped, could be
heard licking its silky fur and cleaning its paws, listened,
sniffed the air, got up and stretched. Then it walked quietly
away, so silently indeed that the drake dared not move for half
an hour, not knowing where or even if it had really gone.

Then, cautiously, he raised his head on his snakelike neck,
looked round, listened, smelt the air. The stench of the beast
was everywhere, but it was growing a little stale already. And
the air smelt thickly now of raw blood. The drake began to
move carefully to and fro, vaguely looking for the others. Like
all natural creatures, he had no interest in or fear of the mess
of blood, bones, and feathers that marked the places where the
lynx had been feeding. The dead did not seem to have any
meaning to the pintail drake.

The lake itself was still empty of birds which had fled from
it to all sorts of hiding places when the killer first approached
the shore. But as the drake stared out across the water, he
saw half a dozen of his kind swimming quietly out from an
inlet farther along the bank. They were alert, nervous, but the
way they dipped their heads to feed showed that they did not
anticipate any instant peril. Then the watching drake saw another sign of safety: the rabbits, which had vanished like
ghosts, had reappeared just as silently and were dancing,
feeding, and jumping along in the moonlight on a bluff two
hundred yards away.

With the absolute suddenness of magic, the rabbits all vanished and the lake was once more empty of birds. The drake sank down in the grass, yet watched keenly through the stems to discover what new peril threatened him and them all. A shiny brown-coated hunting mink hopped down to the lake shore. He traveled as if on springs, taking little spasmodic hops, each one motivated by enormous energy. He pushed off into the water, the gleaming dark back shining. He was about eighteen inches long, and his tail floated, adding nine inches to his length. Flip! He had dived, and the lake was still and empty under the moon. Time passed. Where would he come up? Without a sound, his glimmering head broke the surface, and he had a fish jerking in his jaws. He came ashore, pulled it to bits, ate it, and then went flickering off with those queer spasmodic hops.

Although so much had happened, the northern night was very brief, and already light was in the sky; indeed, although overcome by the brightness of the moon, the day had never really faded completely from the northern rim of the sky. The drake went nervously down to feed. Within a few minutes, the lake was crowded with birds as if nothing had happened, no enemy come to bring death among them. Only they swam in a compact flock, almost half of them at a time keeping stiff-necked watch while the others fed. The drake caught and swallowed a young frog and dug a specially fat worm from the mud where the shore rose over the water.

He still had not seen the little duck. The white mallard was back again, apparently totally unmoved because his mate had been clawed down and eaten by the prowling killer in the night. He still seemed very friendly and kept close to the pintail drake. The pintail, still unable to fly, was somehow more alive this morning, and his wretched and frazzled wings seemed to have acquired a new lightness and sense of life. He moved them, opened and shut them, preened them with ridiculous care.

Then, swimming about the lake or shoving through the grasses, he began intermittently to search for his mate. He was not very greatly moved by her absence. Nonetheless, he desired to find her. She was vaguely necessary sometimes to his sense of completeness and well-being. Sometimes, too, he remembered his fledglings, though they were not now needing any help, being able to fly when their parents could not, and away meeting the adventure of life on their own. At times that day, the drake was powerfully urged to fly high and go away. He did not know where he wished to go, not even in which direction to turn, and he had no power at all to use his molted wings in flight. Yet he felt the urge stirring his whole body, and the lake, which had seemed so utterly contenting to him for so many weeks and to which he had fought his way across three thousand dangerous miles of sky and sea, now appeared frightening and strange.

It was in the afternoon that he noticed his mate, creeping despondently out of some sedges. She stared at him in alarm as if he were a stranger, then scuttled back along a sort of tunnel under the rank grass. He followed, rather nervously in that dim place, and found her crouched with three other ducks in a hollow under the grass. He had hardly had time to shrink down beside them when the white mallard shoved his way in and settled down there too. He was molting badly, but even in eclipse he looked much more handsome in his spotted white than the others did, and he seemed bigger and more confident.

That night, after dark, they emerged to feed. It was past

midnight when they crept out, for the daylight had lingered in the sky. Now, however, because of heavy rain clouds driving in from the southwest, the world was pitchy dark save for a lemon-colored rim of northern sky which seemed to make the trees, the reeds, and the fantastic shapes of the mud bluffs inkier yet.

The wild ducks had not postponed their feeding time by chance. A new and awful feeling had been steadily spreading through the world, for about two hours. At first, they crouched before it, not daring to lift a head from the ground. This was an awe much deeper and more imperious than the natural fear they had felt when the killer approached. From that, flight had in the last moment been possible. Before this emanation from earth and sky and water, nothing could flee.

Yet instinct is very strong, and the need for food and drink and the longing to wash in cool and flowing water after the heat and feverish clamminess of a day of molt at last drove them out. They went in single file, softly, breathlessly, looking neither to right nor left. Any enemy could have picked them up one by one, but the animals as well as the birds were completely and nervelessly subdued.

Over on the distant hills, invisible in the blackness of that brief midnight hour, the wolves were howling as they had never howled since the wild ducks arrived on the marsh. They were lifting their muzzles to the soft darkness, and slowly at first, then swelling, the long howl wailed its way upward into the abyss. First one infinitely lonely cry; then another miles away: then half a dozen together; then solitary and sorrowing cries from all over the hills. There was something eerie in the sound, a frightened appeal from dumb, awed things to an unanswering sky. The air everywhere felt electric, supercharged with unformed emotions and sensations, filled intolerably with a sense of tremendous hurry and of things invisible passing to and fro and leaping from horizon to horizon faster than thought.

The wild ducks, blindly following an instinct which told them they were safer on water than on land, swam out with little, fluttering strokes toward the middle of the lake and crowded there tightly. Usually, their night feeding was accompanied by subdued quacks, plashings, lipplings, and quick, happy movements. Now they floated as if petrified. They did not feed or drink or do anything but crouch on the water waiting with rapidly beating hearts.

Over in the unseen and distant hills, the wolves' ghostly chorus began to rise, hundreds and hundreds of thin cries murmuring from furry throats, then swelling in a panic chorus.

And then that and all other noises ceased abruptly as if an enormous hand had covered the whole earth.

17. *Aurora*

THE UTTER SILENCE that ensued was not a natural silence but an awed immobility in which all the creatures of the wild northland shared. Hunter and hunted shrank alike against the earth. Feeding, journeying, and love-making stopped. It seemed as if the very air was stilled.

After that sacred pause, a long green streamer took form and waved enormous across the sky, still in perfect silence in which not a leaf moved. The lower edge of that divine scarf of light was perhaps a hundred miles up in the air. It swelled unbearably, gathering intensity as it did so, until the upper edge was at least five hundred miles high, and the luminous glow was so intense that the patches of green in the pintails' wings could be clearly distinguished on the grayish feathers, shining with a beauty they never had possessed before. The whole lake and marsh were clearly visible, but that great strange light among the darkness of the world made the place unearthly with a loveliness that cried: "Thy Kingdom come!"

Then the luminous presence in the sky began to change its form. Shafts of white light hundreds of miles long stabbed out from it like searchlights pointing at different angles and walked solemnly about the heavens. There was an overwhelming impression that they went majestically with a great rolling sound, yet there was no sound at all about the world or in the skies over the world.

The glowing light slowly took the form of a curtain so pure and immense that it seemed to hide the portals of Paradise. There were great folds or flutings in it, high up the sky; the lower edge now stretched round the horizon at about the same height above the earth all round the band, but the upper edge was triumphantly arched. The wild ducks, looking up, saw as it were almost over them great folds in the auroral drapery, into which they could see, so that the fluting of the folds seemed to gather upward toward a point from which they hung in the air.

Slowly and splendidly, the whole aurora began to move across the silent sky. The luminosity of the enormous curtain changed from faint to deeper yellow-green, and all the lower edge glowed a glorious red, shading to blue, gray, and violet. The rays and flutings of the bands seemed to swing over and wave as if at the passing of a mighty rushing wind.

Meanwhile, the wild ducks and all the creatures of land and water illuminated by the aurora trembled at the flowing up from the earth and down from the skies of a strange and irresistible magnetism that held all their bodies still in thrall. It felt as though something gentle but all-powerful stroked feather and fur and as though life was actually renewing its mysterious current in their limbs and hearts.

Many times since the wild ducks had first alighted on this northern marsh, a much paler aurora had touched the night sky with color, and sometimes its presence had been felt in the sunshiny light of day. But those visitations were no more than warnings before which the things of the wilderness briefly bowed their heads and then pursued their own activities again. In the spell of glorious Summer which had lasted through the birds' nesting time, the nights had been hardly apparent for the sun scarcely set, and usually the moon or stars had silvered the brief moving empire of the dark. Tonight, everything was different. The cloudy blackness spoke plainly of a darker, wintry season that was to come, and the great release of magnetism from the earth's body proclaimed change, retraction, and swift departure.

As the magnificence of the light began to fade, great new flashes of color shot silently across it over the crouching world. Then, with dramatic and mysterious suddenness, it vanished away, and through its paling shone sharp and silvery the beam of a single star. Still, the world remained silent and motionless, and the wild ducks floated in a tight group on the center of the lake. Other stars came out swiftly as if by magic; the whole sky filled with them, twinkling and glittering through clear air from which the going of the aurora seemed to have swept every trace of cloud. Each star was reflected in the steady lake water. Trees stood inky black; grasses were faintly white on one side and behind them stretched limitless shadows: the fantastic shapes of the mud castles in the marsh seemed to change silently and be different every time they were looked at again. Presently, the first paleness of morning was about, and the ducks were feeding, furtively and with as little noise as possible, each one still quivering with the released magnetism that had caused or attracted that glowing glory in the skies.

In the early light, they saw, standing as suddenly on the bank of the lake as if they had been conjured up from the mud, two large bull elks. They were poised about ten yards from each other, motionless, regardant. The palmate projecting antlers seemed too long and heavy even for those massive and short-necked heads. Although this was very early in the Autumn for them to quarrel, the abnormal release of magnetism from the ground had apparently frightened or excited them, and now that they had come so suddenly face to face, neither was willing to retreat.

One, slightly larger and shaggier than the other, pawed with a thin foreleg and uttered a low cry, whose sound resembled the rubbing of two sticks together. This was apparently a challenge, for the other, at a speed almost unbelievable in so ungainly a beast, lowered its head and charged. The great antlers crashed together harshly, and for a minute the two beasts strained every sinew and applied every pound of their great weight, each trying to force the other back.

Very slightly, at last, the bigger elk which had begun the attack seemed to sway. Then his outthrust feet slid a little, only a few inches, but immediately the other redoubled the pressure in a frantic attempt to gain ground. Perhaps the older animal had more experience of such fights and could use wile; without warning, he swung his head, disengaged antlers, and, as his opponent rushed triumphantly forward, slashed at him with a razorlike hoof that cut a scarlet wound down his ribs.

Yet the younger brute made use of his superior quickness by half turning as he ran forward, and his antlers thumped with a sickening sound against his enemy's massive shoulder, driving him staggering and limping back. They turned at once fully facing each other, but paused. Both had been hurt. Blood dripped onto the moss while the bigger elk shifted his weight off his hurt shoulder and tossed his head as if to invite a renewal of the combat. With a fierce mutual grunt, they crashed together again.

This time, by some trick of turn and thrust, the bigger animal drove one side of his antlers through the other's guard and got home squarely on his bony forehead with a sound like a sledge hammer hitting a post. The victim swayed, then went down on one knee, instantly jumping up again as his enemy rounded to finish him off with a rush intended to smash in his side or disjoint his thick neck. That rush was not quite fast enough; the younger elk stepped aside and slashed out with both forehoofs which ripped the other's shoulder and foreleg to the bone.

Again, they stood staring at each other, their breath panting, their eyes starting. Each was seriously hurt. Warily, the older animal glanced round, perhaps to find where the female was for whom he thought he was fighting or perhaps with a desire for flight. The other, earlier in that primitive combat, would have seized that moment's inattention to charge, but the blow on his head had almost stunned him, and he stood snorting heavily, unable to move and, now the threat to his life was momentarily abated, almost unable to see. He slowly moved his head from side to side, trying to clear it, bewildered, swaying, yet full of deadly strength even now.

His opponent, swift and silent almost as a shadow, spun round and galloped off, the big feet touching the ground with apparent lightness, the ungainly head tilted. Away he went through the blackened tree stumps where the fire had been, running as fast as a horse. The other lumbered in halfhearted pursuit that was never intended to bring him into battle range; he had had enough of that sudden and deadly encounter, but he bellowed to claim a doubtful triumph.

The wild ducks watched him go; and when the marsh was quiet again, they sailed in to the side of the lake, climbed

ashore, and dispersed into their hideaways for the day. The
four ducks, the pintail drake, and the white mallard crept
into their sedgy lair and crouched down to sleep the day away.
Yet there was less despondency among them that day. It was
as if the aurora had released a new eagerness of spirit among
them, as well as painfully intensified the restless urge that was
now beginning to be apparent among all the wild ducks. In
the warm and dreamy hours, as they pressed together for mutual comfort, they heard a flight of big birds pass unseen
through the sky outside that grassy cavern where they hid, and
at the sound the pintail drake stood up and stirred his ragged
wings. He no longer felt that he could not fly; now he knew
with wild impatience that he would fly, that his wings would
bear him up, even if not at this moment. And he was consumed
by the ardency of his desire to fly, not merely to get into the
air but to go away, to go somewhere else. Imitative as all birds
are, the white mallard also stretched his wings.

In the days that followed, the pintail drake found his feathers smoothing down once more. He had ceased to drop feathers wherever he went, and he was losing the meek, apologetic
air of a molting bird and regaining his shy, wild courage. One
day, he went out remembering his brood. He recalled them
as half-feathered youngsters and could not find them among
the slender, graceful young birds who played and swam together with no interest in their ragged elders. Once or twice,
in the swift turn of a graceful and shining head or the glance
of a brilliant eye, he thought he remembered, but the young
bird stared at him hostilely and coldly, and he turned away
and pretended to be interested in something else.

This period of confinement to the ground made the older
birds fat and strong. They could feed well, and they slept

almost all the time they were not feeding. Gradually their
feathers grew again, then they seemed to come suddenly into
a plumage adequate at least for them to show themselves pub-
licly once more. They strode about in the early Autumn sunshine, feeling the movements of their new wing feathers and
tails, sometimes swimming, chattering excitedly. All were restless, eager, unwilling to stay a moment in one place.

For a long time the pintail drake had resembled his mate
in color. But now new vermiculated feathers showed on his
back and sides, his white neck stripe was becoming obvious
once more, and the long tail feathers he had always carried
so proudly were growing. Again and again, the drake stretched
and tried his wings, though still he could not fly. Then, one
sunny morning, he jumped up from the ground and discovered, half in alarm, that he was flying. He beat the air faster
than the fastest of his normal flight; he stretched his neck in
front and his tail behind, frantically elongating himself to
offer less wind resistance; he skated at thirty feet up or so half
across the lake, then stretched out his wings and glided down
onto the water with a heavy flop.

He was utterly fatigued, and his heart beat as if it would
burst, but he had flown, and later that day he was up on the
wing for another short and dangerous flight. Because of his
extra effort, he seemed to have developed racy lines in the air,
despite the heavy feeding and lack of exercise of the past weeks.

The mallard drake was only a day after him in finding once
more the use of his wings, and in the next day or two most of
the drakes were able to fly. In noisy and happy parties, they
began to fly abroad looking for strange titbits of food. There
was an afternoon when the white mallard, flying high, spotted
a dead salmon lying on its side on the mud far up the river and

swooped down to examine it, accompanied by a dozen greedy companions. The others were afraid, but the white bird stalked up to the great fish, struck it with his bill, then gouged a lump of rotting flesh out of it. He swallowed the morsel with delight and set to in earnest. The others drew near, fascinated, then began to eat too. They were furtive, but the mallard was shameless; he gorged himself till he could scarcely walk. They flew home very slowly over the marshes; and as they flew, two of the drakes uttered on the wing the thrilling whistle that had marked the beginning of their northward migration flight. All the flying birds stared about them as they winged their way high over the mud flats; they glanced at each other and round the horizon as though they had heard some stranger call. For this note differed subtly from the usual pintail whistle; it was shriller, clearer, much more imperative and strong. At its sound, they quickened their wingbeats to top speed. The white mallard was left slowly flapping behind, falling farther and farther into the rear, till he was at last out of sight. The others scurried on, circled the marsh that was their home, and came down at tremendous speed onto the mud.

At this time, the pintail drake's mate was like a pleasant acquaintance; he seldom sought her company or she his, but they recognized each other when they met and were very friendly, much more friendly than either was with any other bird. Yet, in the main, the drakes hunted together and the ducks were usually to be found vaguely in attendance on the young birds of the year. They did not clearly know their own offspring, but were solicitous, fussy, anxious to watch and be near the new generation, who paid them scant attention but played together all over lake and ground and sky.

One morning, the almost endless fine and sunny spell of

Arctic Summer broke. Gray clouds came driving in from the sea, scudding before a soft, enticing wind, and gray sheeting warm rain poured down onto the marsh. The wild ducks greeted this rain with joy. They circled up in it, shot at great speed through it on level flights, and pirouetted in the air with sheer instinctive delight.

The pintail drake, his wings fully restored though he still looked very different from the graceful and lovely bird who had flown north, played and soared with the rest. Something was released in him, some wild urge that had been overlaid with all the trivial cares of nest building and observing downy young and crouching furtive beneath the grasses during his molt. He felt—*free!* Free of this cloying place, free of the care of others, free to fly, free to go—to go!

Opening his bill as he raced down the rain-sweet air, he uttered the call of flight and freedom, the strangely moving piping whistle whose sound echoed the thin wild stir of distance and the song of the wind over the seas.

18. Go from Here!

No ONE KNOWS the reasons that cause untold millions of birds to flow to and fro across the earth's surface in migratory movements that sometimes take a single bird more than twenty-five thousand miles in a year. The wild ducks in their northern nesting ground grew restless, at the earliest hints of Autumn in the air; many factors contributed to that unease.

Ultraviolet radiation decreasing in the air as the sunlight began to retire southward registered its secret effect on the birds' preen glands, and as they passed their feathers through their bills in preening, something was different and disturbing. Some other quality of difference, too, was apparent to their intensely seeing eyes, some change in the hours of light and dark that warned them that they must soon be on their way.

Their food was as plentiful as—perhaps more plentiful than —it had ever been since their arrival. The temperature was higher than when they came and in no way caused them the least discomfort. They were not fleeing from Winter as we know it, because, for tens of thousands of generations, Winter had been unknown to such birds as these who spent each half of every year in a warm climate. They could have no conscious knowledge of something they had never experienced, and so there could be no reasoned intention in their act of avoidance. Custom itself must be ruled out, since in many breeds of birds, the young of a season fly on migration unaccompanied by elders or on a route different from that used by their parents, though they reach independently the same goal. These young birds were not taught their way over hundreds of miles of strange land or sea; they had never passed that way before or learned from others of their race any necessity to leave their birthplace. Failure of food supplies out of season or abnormally heavy food supplies present at migration time do not affect the birds' departure, nor does unseasonable weather cause any but the slightest change. Sexual changes in the birds do not explain away migration, since immature young birds are affected equally with their adult elders. How deep is the instinct of migration may be shown by taking the eggs of a nonmigratory mallard and hatching them in a nest of a migratory type, when the young birds migrate with their "hosts."

For days before their southward flight, the great flock of pintails on the northern marsh were actively preparing for their new adventure. Never was there such a polishing and preening of newly grown flight feathers that had replaced the worn and rubbed plumage of yesteryear. The refeathering was by no means yet complete, and the pintail drake and his mate had not yet put on the fullness and beauty of their winter plumage, but they were able to fly as well as ever, for their wing feathers, though still dull and spotted, were strong and capable of all the stresses of migration flight.

Before this southern move, there was much more evidence of activity than before the long northern journey. They had all exploded into motion together then and gone without

warning, but now there was joyous rushing about, much pre-
paratory long-distance day-flying southward as if to prospect
the route or say goodbye to favored feeding spots, and continual whistling on that high, excitable note that betokened
the advent of a great exploit.

Perhaps, during these days of preparing, some powers unknown to humanity were being focused and organized to enable these wanderers of the skies to find their way. For on this
southward journey, most of the traveling would be done at
night. Birds do not see well at night, and visual recognition
of the contours and objects on the way would be out of the
question when there was neither moonlight nor starlight and
when, as was bound to be at this time of year, there was often
driving rain or fog as well. Perhaps, up there in the northland
that was still so summery in appearance, the wild ducks somehow concentrated their mysterious powers so that they could
safely fly over thousands of miles to a sought and known destination, even when they could not see the way they flew or the
dangerously changing contours under them or even estimate
the shapes of wind currents flowing off those lands and seas.

There were other changes, too, from the order of the northward flight. Then, mated pairs had flown together and the
sexes had mixed freely in the air. Now, the males assembled
more or less in one flock and the females and young in another. There was frequent individual overlapping; the pintail
drake and his mate were to see a good deal of each other on
the route, yet in general there was a sense of division during
a considerable part of the southward flight. Again, there was
not the same urgency as had driven them north. This time, they
were prepared to delay, almost to make holiday, where food
was plentiful and safety seemed assured.

Far more than before, it was as though they were preparing for a pleasure trip rather than being dragged at great speed through the skies by some strange and invisible compulsive force. How were they to find their way south to those very brakes from which they had set out? Undoubtedly, recognition of outstanding physical features—coast lines, hills, groups of trees, and river courses—would help them to check their route. Probably, like certain insects, they could keep flying at a relatively constant angle to the sun's rays, compensating by the bird's acute time sense for the spinning of the earth beneath them. Almost certainly, they could direct themselves from wave patterns on the sea and compensate for wind drift by watching these patterns. Their strong form vision would help them to fly at night by the stars. Possibly, too, they have some magnetic sense, even though experiments with attached magnets have not given any results. Their superhuman sensitivity to the colors red and orange might enable them to see through fog to a greater degree than humanity can. Possibly, they possess a "radar" sense, as bats are known to do, warning them of solid objects ahead or under them and perhaps even of the contours of land over which they are passing.

The wild ducks prepared for their southward journey, sublimely trustful of the instinct that for untold millions of years had guided their race. For them, there were no calculations and no thoughts of the route; all they had to do was to jump into the air, and their bodies would swing in the right direction, their wings would desire to beat, and their tail feathers automatically adjust to keep them true in their unseen and unmapped path.

Part of the preparation for the long flight was a certain voluntary penance in the midst of almost too plentiful food on that northern breeding ground. It seemed as if Nature had suddenly put forth her strength to tempt these visitors to stay too long. When the white mallard gorged himself with dead salmon, he could fly only slowly and only for a mile or two at a time. A day or so later, he discovered a water plant with succulent seeds, and managed—by a prodigious effort—to take in at one feeding over one hundred thousand of them, stuffing his stomach and gullet so tight that he could not even rise from the ground. The forgetfulness of nesting duties had caused a gluttony in him which the pintails never quite approached—though they could cram themselves on occasions also. There was an avid desire, on these last days, to fill themselves up with mosquito larvae, always a favorite food.

This gormandizing came to an abrupt end for all of them when the migration restlessness spread. They ate well but sparingly, drank more deeply than usual, washed with extreme care and increased frequency. There was something of the solemnity of a sacrament in these last days of preparation; and indeed, it was necessary for them to devote themselves, for migration is a process very costly of bird life and not to be undertaken in anything but a perfection of physical strength and instinctive concentration.

On the last day, it was obvious that some dramatic change was about to take place. That day, a perfect sunny farewell for them, none flew even half a mile from the lake. A great concourse of birds, divided into two parts, the older males in one and the rest in the other, swam in very close order on the rippling surface, so tightly that in places not even a hand could have been put between the feathered sides. Although, as a rule, they mostly slept or rested during a good part of the day, on this occasion all were silently wakeful and watchful. Their

heads were turned south, and they seemed to stare with eagerness into the southern sky, more especially at midday when the
light was most intense. When one or another swam restlessly
round to face another way, it very soon spun about to the south
once more, as if compelled.

The washing and feeding that evening began before the sun
set. All over the lake, there was a shivering busyness, and
though they ate well, they were reluctant to dip their heads
too deep and hastily glanced at one another whenever they
were not actually seizing their food.

It was a night of bright and silvery moonlight; the whole
round disk of the moon was showing clearly in the sky before
the daylight had faded. Through a pale horizon mist, the low
moon looked enormous and seemed to possess spectral luminosity. Its beams shone across the silent world, showing the
burned-out bones of the spruce forest, the blackened edge of
the marsh, and the silver rim of lake water, the whole of whose
middle was taken up with a closely packed and waiting armada
of wild birds.

It seemed that they were waiting for something, and it was
when the first brightening moonbeam crept silvery onto the
water at the lake's edge that hundreds of the pintails flew up,
with a tremendous rush of wings, followed at intervals of half
a minute by further great groups, unrolling as it were off the
water and into the sky. This more orderly departure was to
some extent forced upon them by the huge number of birds
taking part in the migration flight. The flock that came north
had been a very large one, but now it was multiplied by five
or six, and as thousand after thousand mounted from the
marshland, a gigantic formation took shape amidst a sibila-
tion of feather-swept air that became almost deafening.

The parent males took the lead, the females and young birds dropping into place behind them. These nestlings of the year had never flown in long-distance formation before; when going about the marshland in gangs, they flew in tight, irregularly shaped groups; yet now every proud young bird fell instinctively into order and accepted instantly and without teaching or experiment the peculiar rhythmic wingbeat of migration journeying. The huge echelon of birds stretched across the night sky, and whistling calls ran thrillingly from end to end of the serried lines. There is no question but that birds possess a rudimentary language and use their calls deliberately to communicate with one another; their cries of warning, anger, instruction, and others that are purely conversational and allow groups to keep in touch, are all well known. These flying thousands in the dim moonlit sky called to dress their formation, to maintain even distance, and also because they could not stop from crying their pleasure to the moon and stars.

Again, there thrilled through all of them that sense of a common purpose and all the delight of simultaneous submission to a universal desire. Birds which cannot sing, and many which can, find their highest expression of bliss in the urgency of rapid flight, even alone, and ten thousand times more poignant when ten thousand fly as one. The ripples of the aerial sea caressed them as they flew; at almost a mile a minute, the landscape under them unrolled its moonlit beauties: new scents wafted up to them; and all ahead, over a time and distance that seemed infinite to them, there was something glorious and something new.

They traveled only a short distance that night, compared with the enormous hops of their more urgent northern journey. They descended on a lake hardly big enough to contain them and began feeding on the buds and fronds of water plants. Owing to their immense number, there was neither space nor food enough for them all, and after a few minutes, some hundreds of the old drakes, with the white mallard and the pintail at their head, rose above the trees to swing a mile aside to another little lake. They knew it was there, though they had never visited it or even seen it. Race memory from progenitors who had used that lake for overflow feeding on the southward flight, led them unerringly over the treetops and down onto water where there was more than enough for them all. In bachelor freedom they ate and chattered quietly, splashed and sat up staring, explored the lake edges and ventured a little way, very cautiously, ashore. The white mallard, as usual, was the boldest adventurer among them. He it was who went out of sight alone, a thing no pintail would have done without abnormal enticement. He came back once, then again.

Once more he wandered into the dark and moonlit patterning of the forest. He walked quietly over soft and fragrant mold, digging lazily here and there. Suddenly, he sank down close to the earth as if his legs had given way beneath him. There was a smell in the air, rank and strong, between him and the lake. With a swift turn of the head, he glanced among the branches to seek a way to fly. But here the trees were laced together; there was no room for his long wings to pass. He dared not run, for the sound would carry to raised ears and bring death springing on padded feet.

It seemed to him that a long time passed while he waited for the rush, the blinding snap, the pumping away of his own hot lifeblood. But nothing happened. He was downwind of the fox, and so was saved—for the moment. He heard, infinitely softly, the feet of the hunter going slyly away. The stench grew fainter, yet a ghost of it remained. There was no sound now from the lake or from the forest above him. Others besides himself had heard what he had heard.

At last, he began to move with infinite stealth among the black tree trunks toward a clearing. He waited there, his wings tense, ready to fly. But the fox had gone. The lore of the wild told him not to fly unless in great need, for the sweep of his wings would bring the fox quietly back again. So he walked the way he had come, listening, staring, smelling the air, and at last came out on the lake.

The other wild ducks were well out in the center, startled by distant movements in the woods but not actively alarmed. The white drake swam to them. Immediately, they knew from his tense bearing that a killer was on the prowl. They wished to continue feeding and resting; if they flew up and back to the other lake, the fox would follow them.

They took another course of defensive action, one rare with wild ducks yet well known to them all and valuable in just such an emergency as this. A snowy owl had been hooting from the head of this lake, where the water narrowed into a smaller pool. Intently, the flotilla of birds turned and swam, in very close formation, right up into the top pool, almost under the tree where the big ghostly figure sat.

They were themselves somewhat afraid of this strange, silent night bird, more than two feet tall, immensely strong and capable of bursts of fury unsurpassed by any inhabitant of the wild. In the presence of a big owl, the ducks always mobbed together for safety; it was not wise to be alone when hunger drove the nocturnal hunter to extremes. While they were in a mob, however, he would not disturb them, and, what was more important, the fox dared not come near them there. Among the woodland creatures, each has its own hunting ground, and though occasionally there is trespassing, in general a fox stays uneasily clear of a big owl's territory.

There was utter silence as the formation of wild ducks swam up under the uncomfortable sacredness of the white owl's domain. It watched them from its great, ringed eyes, never stirring a single feather. It took in a sweep of moonlit forest, watching for anything that moved—watching especially for the slinking rufous silhouette of a fox. Its long-nailed talons gripped the branch on which it sat: its curved and horny beak opened a little in a tiny snuffling, more threatening and hungry than any scream.

19. Death Flies by Day

THE WILD DUCKS sat very still that night on the water under the tree where the great white owl looked out. They made no further attempt to feed, and they dared not sleep. They bunched tightly together, with necks stiff and eyes searching the darkness of the woods, and often turning uneasily upward.

Almost at once, they became aware of the presence of the fox. He was not near enough to do them any harm, but he was watching them from farther down the lake, with that dreadful patience so essential to those who live by killing. He made no sound, and he could not be seen. He was skillfully placed so that his scent could not carry to the birds. Yet they knew he was there, licking his lips and watching and sniffing them, watching them perhaps through crannies between leaves. He was waiting till the owl should go hunting.

Tall, white, silent as a ghost, the owl looked out across the forest. Once or twice, he wheezed out that almost inaudible snuffling noise. Then the silence was split by his whistling hooting that seemed to undulate for miles over the uneven ground through the trees. From far away came an answer, several times repeated. The owl ruffled up all his feathers noiselessly and leaned forward, hunching his shoulders. Then he launched himself off his branch and slid down the night air with no more disturbance than if he had been a blown breath of mist and was gone.

The ducks seemed to become tense. They looked above them into the sky, marking invisible ways they would fly if the slightest inimical sound reached them. They closely examined the ripples of the dark water lest those ripples should be dividing round the brown head of a fox allowing himself to drift to them in the flow of the lake, without moving paw or back. The muscles of their breasts pringled in case the red enemy should dive and swim underwater toward them. They suspected every sound they heard and pried the silences in alarm for sounds they did not hear, instinctively matching his cunning with theirs and alarmed because his devices were endless and incalculable.

Among the noises of the night, the little whisperings of leaves, the tiny rustle of mice, the light sound as a frog leaped and landed, the stealthy passing of some land animal, and the tip-tip, tip-tip, tip-tip of a rat drinking, they heard a desolate little shriek some distance away. And just after it, they all realized that the fox was shifting his position, drifting as it were much nearer. They stiffened to fly. Then, again without sound, the great white owl sailed over their heads, holding a dying young rabbit in his talons. He landed in a crotch of a great tree, set down the rabbit, and they heard its gasp as he tore its head off. The ripping and swallowing continued for a minute. Then there was silence.

The fox had sunk with his chest to the earth. He was in the forbidden territory and knew it. He dared not go back, for fear of calling attention to himself; yet he knew that the owl probably realized exactly where he was. A drop of blood dripped fatly from the branch and hit the leaves on the ground below. The ducks sat stiffly still well out on the water away from the banks.

For a long time, the owl sat staring at the place where the fox, though invisible from the tree, crouched without movement. Two hours passed. The stillness was such that there might have been no owl, fox, or ducks within a mile. The fox's red eyes narrowed and glittered, and his loose lips several times rolled back from his teeth in a snarl. He was becoming more and more dangerously cramped. He dared not stay too long in this immobile state, or he would be unable to fight to his best if the owl came down on him. His jaws, strong enough to break a man's armbone, slavered as he watched the ducks, whom he could quite clearly see though they could not see him.

Again, the owl leaned forward and made the tiny whickering sound. The fox, watching, saw his deadly opponent leap off the branch and apparently sail straight at him; he sprang up to meet the attack, jaws wide and feet striking, but the huge white phantom passed swiftly six feet above, so high that his savage jump merely looked ridiculous; the owl whisked away through the trees and out of sight. The fox, in anger, turned and ran with hardly more sound than the other, but the ducks, their heads held stiffly up, heard his going for a mile, and he was still running then.

After that deadly warning gesture, the owl did not even turn to see whether it had been effective. It flew out of sight and earshot and did not return until morning was paling the eastern sky. The drakes had been furtively feeding; now they rose together and flew back to the bigger lake where the rest of the flock still sailed. The drakes did not descend but circled high in the air, and as if in answer to that signal, the thousands below leaped up and joined them at a thousand feet above the wood.

For a week, they loitered in that lovely northland, as if reluctant to leave it altogether even though they had found purpose enough to start their long southward flight. They reached the coast and followed its course, sometimes sleeping for a day in a sheltered inlet, flying mostly by night. At last, they came to the place where their route took them away from the land and out over the sea.

Here they paused for a few days. The final breakaway from their northern homeland was postponed, while they explored in parties for two or three hundred miles around. There seemed no perils here, and still there was no visible sign of coming Winter. Other senses than that of sight were, however, warning them that they must very soon end their stay. The light was changing about them in a way visible only to their extraordinarily light-sensitive eyes. Something living had gone out of it completely. They could see that the absence of this quality in the light was affecting the leaves and grasses; their color was becoming almost imperceptibly darker, and their edges were pale. The water tasted different, not so sparkling as it had been. It felt colder to the sailing breast. At dawn and dusk, and more so about an hour before dawn, there was something in the air, a damper and more still feeling.

One evening when they were feeding, the millions of wild geese who had passed them on their northern journey went by overhead, honking, their great wings swishing, the formation seeming to cover the whole sky. The immense company took several minutes to pass, and the noise of their going faded away southward across the sea.

Half an hour later, the wild ducks were following them

along that invisible migration highroad. The calm sea shone
dully in starlight, stretching out endlessly to every horizon,
before and behind and to each side. The huge echelon of
flying ducks seemed to stand still in the midst of unvarying
views of the greatness of the ocean; though they were traveling at almost a mile a minute, nothing appeared to change.

This time, in their great sea crossing, they were fortunate
in having mild and peaceful weather. All, even the young
birds of the year who did not know where or why they were
flying, exulted wildly now they were really under way southward. Despite the succession of hour after hour spent in winging south at almost the top speed of which they were capable,
they found time for beautiful aerial traceries and patternings.
Groups of birds replacing the echelon's leading edge, instead
of speeding straight into their places, poured like lovely living
fountains up the sky and rolled over and down; others, swooping till their breasts were wet with spray from the wave tops,
wove in and out of curving figures as though performing
measures in a complicated winged dance. Through the dim
haze of starlight blue, hundreds of feathered bodies billowed
light as smoke, the luster on some young bird's patch of wing
color gleaming as he swiftly turned.

They flew all through the night and saw the morning come
up in splendor over the tossing sea horizon while still no land
was in sight. The pintail drake and his duck had found each
other again and were flying with wing tips almost touching at
each downward sweep. The air was cold and lovely bearing
them up, and the whirr of wings seemed to enclose them in a
perfect and secret world. Not far behind them, challenging
already for a place among his elders, was the strongest of the
young drakes of their nestlings, his eyes shining, his slim young

wings beating with a confidence that only belongs to the young.

When the huge flock of birds saw ahead of them at last the purple mistiness which betokened the mainland point from which the parents had flown north, they did not seek a resting place although they were weary with that tremendous stretch of journeying. They wanted to fly on; the older birds knew a big lake, a nodal point of migration for many breeds of wild ducks, where they could delay for a week or two, feed, rest, and enjoy above all that gregarious delight of their kind in meeting tens of thousands of others who were also on their way back from the northern adventure. This autumn gossip and fraternization with uncountable legions of other travelers was something never to be missed.

They came to this lake during the afternoon, and when from afar they first caught sight of its vicinity, it was like some place whirling with the dust of an atomic explosion. Something had excited or alarmed the enormous assembly of birds already there, or perhaps they were flying for sheer delight through the liquid sunshine of that Autumn afternoon. Over an area two miles long by three broad, it looked as if there were not space to put one more bird, so closely were they flying, idly circling and gliding in a swirling mass that began a hundred feet from the water and seemed to stretch a mile upward into the sky.

As the new arrivals poured down under that moving cloud, they saw a chain of small lakes in the midst of bushy and marshy country that shone with colors like the tablecloth of God. The string of lakes were as blue as a sapphire necklace in sunlight, glittering and flashing; the green was of that lush richness that only marshland country can ever show: and the bushes which softly dotted it were just beginning to blaze with fire glows from the first frosts. Yellowed, encrimsoned, piercing scarlet and shadowed blue, some looked as if they had been painted with blood and gold, while others seemed to have been transfixed in the act of bursting into flames.

With a whispering rush of wings, the thousands of the new contingent of wild ducks sailed down to rest on one of the lakes, and as though their descent had been an awaited sign, all the rest began to settle down toward the lake surfaces. The entire heaven was alive with moving, feathery shapes all sweeping downward; myriads of graceful birds, some with blue patches, some with green, some with short wings and others almost as pointed-winged as hawks, some large and some small, came to rest with such a chattering, piping, splashing, and playing as if the sunshine itself had broken into a million living pieces.

Never was such a calling and crying, never such a glancing of thousands of shy and flashing eyes, a ruffling of feathers and half display of unconscious beauty, a turning and rising and falling on the constantly agitated water. Always feeling uneasiness alone and safety in numbers, all the birds lost every vestige of fear, swam to and fro in that joyous multitude. The pintails, with their brilliant dark hazel eyes, white neck stripes, elegant shape, and the rich golden-green beauty spots on their wings, were as proud and friendly as any, uttering their low chattering note of welcome and greeting as they moved to and fro.

Having exhausted their immediate excitement, most of them slept after their long oversea flight. At evening, they awoke and fed on water insects, caddis worms, seeds, roots, and pondweed tips. Then came more dozing, with intervals of feeding, and the whole surface of the lakes seemed alive with birds, some floating with heads under wings, some eagerly dipping for food, many moving about for sheer pleasure in looking at and showing themselves off to each other, all through the peaceful night.

The day or two that followed were dream days of idling about the marsh and in nearby woods, fattening on beechnuts, looking for young acorns, digging out creatures that were settling down to hibernate, scaring each other playfully, swooping in fantastic figures around other groups in the air, whirling from pond to pond to try to scare tens of thousands into half-timid, half-merry flight. There were leeches to be caught and flies to be snapped down on the wing or while they paused for a second on a grass-blade. There were shadowless middays spent basking in the sun on the water, and there was an afternoon of whispering rain.

All of them knew they must sweep on southward, and the need for it sharpened the deliciousness of lotus-eating, while each night the colors of the leaves were painted by light frosts to a more unearthly loveliness. The pintail drake and his little duck went everywhere together, and she sometimes vaguely recognized the swift, slim, passing gracefulness of one of their brood.

Then came a night of dreamy stillness, followed by a misty and magic day. Just as the evening light began to outline objects more blackly, the pintail drake lifted his head nervously. What looked like a log about twenty-five feet long was drifting very slowly through some tall rushes at one edge of the lake. It was black, deep in the water, hardly stirring; yet there was something about it that alarmed him. Watching it, he saw a sudden glitter from its side, which instantly vanished.

The men in the shooting punt had been lying down, one of

them sculling imperceptibly over the stern while the other had risked a glance through field glasses. In the front of the punt was a big gun, and one man held the lanyard that would fire it. They were perhaps two hundred yards from the nearest edge of that huge assembly of sleeping ducks, and very, very slowly drifting nearer.

The drake sat with his head up, watching. His mate nervously stiffened, following his gaze. Yet the punt, just like any half-submerged log, looked innocent and empty. Other birds in the vicinity stirred and began to stare. But they were not the nearest to the slowly drifting thing that was every moment creeping a little and a little nearer. Most of the birds were either asleep or drowsy. Thousands sat on the water with heads unsuspiciously tucked under wings, oblivious to danger. Those watching became very tense, and all were completely silent. In that silence, the lap of the water and the very faint sighing of the wind were the only sounds.

Another shape—log or enemy?—appeared behind the first. Then another and another. The pintail duck jerked her head. Her feathers seemed to lift. She was watching with the most intent focus of her piercing eyes the nearest of those advancing threats. It was less than a hundred yards from the nearest edge of the area so thickly covered by sleeping birds when the little duck saw the movement of an arm over the stern of the forward boat.

It seemed that, as she leaped vertically upward into the air, the entire lake exploded. Thousands of other watching birds were moving at the first whip of sound of her first wing stroke, and before those wings had fallen, the myriads of sleepers were on the wing also. As they went, the man at the lanyard pulled back his hand sharply, and there was a multiple roar, while

great stabs of red flame shot from all the boats toward the fleeing multitude in the sky.

The whole world seemed filled with terrifying noises; scarlet terror stalked from horizon to horizon; the pintails bunched
in wild flocks; some of the other ducks raced up the wind, some
sideslipped and skidded avoiding imaginary pursuers. Panic
seemed to fill the air with whistling lead and those stabbing
thin flames of death, and the pintail pair saw below and beside them bodies falling, down puffing and flying loose, blood
spitting and dropping from feathered sides.

20. *The Lighthouse*

THE PANIC let loose by the roar of the duck shooters' guns broke up the huge concourse of wild ducks once more into groups of separate breeds. The pintails—those who had escaped the holocaust—bunched together and tore across the evening sky, never heeding their direction, at a speed of well over seventy miles an hour. The pumping memory of flame and smoke and the thin-whistling flying death that had cut through them and hurtled so many dead or dying to crash on the lake waters haunted and pursued them. For over an hour, they raced away pell-mell, in no formation, every bird for itself, following one another and keeping together only because their gregarious nature made fear even more horrible alone. They traveled about eighty miles, unaware of the way they went, going at right angles to their southward route, and found themselves well out over the sea again before any effort was made to reform into an echelon or seek an intentional route.

Even then, a deadly fear of renewal of that shockingly sudden attack in a place they had for generations known to be perfectly safe forced them like a repelling magnet to curve away from the southward line they would otherwise have

taken. Great directional bulges of this sort do at times super-
impose themselves on age-old known migration routes; if
it were not that wild things learned swiftly to curve away from
dangers, whole breeds would die out. Other migration groups
of pintails would use that pretty chain of little lakes for many
years to come, but they would be birds from different starting
points; those from the areas from which these set out would
always, now, swerve away from a point pregnant for them and
their descendants with the threat of death.

So, of course, the leaders had to devise and adventure
along a new and unexplored portion of the mapless aerial
road. Their general direction would still be southward; they
would, in the end, alight at the same lakes and ponds from
which they had originally started north. But this detour would
first have to be covered, partly by instinct but largely by swift
and intelligent observation and adaption to whatever perils
and benefits might be discovered along its course.

The huge formation of birds was reshaped in a few moments
of common and unguided consent, the old drakes in a squadron ahead, the ducks and all the young of the year following.
All, even the young birds, were stretching out eager heads and
sensing with every nerve in their bodies for that "road of
feeling" through the skies that would lead them eventually
to their southern home. As a magnet needle quivers before
swinging inevitably to the north, so every bird of the flying
thousands felt the air about them on this side and on that, to
distill from its million wild messages the invisible, inaudible
yet commanding impulses that would draw them to the southern home of their tribe that more than half their number had
never seen.

In a single startling movement, as the sense of direction

silently but compellingly flowed into their nerves, the whole enormous cohort swung round and began confidently to wing their way high above the trackless sea, at an angle to their former line of flight. This new line would carry them away from the retreating coast. None of them had ever been here before, and by no power of memory or deduction could they tell whether there would be land ahead of them or whether they might fly on over water till exhaustion killed them. Yet something deeper than experience and more positive than measurement informed them that this was the way that they must go.

Night had fallen over the sea, and soon after the sun sank behind the tossing horizon, there came a sudden blatter of rain. The pintail drake and the white mallard were flying shoulder to shoulder at the point of the drakes' formation. In the rush from the guns, they had escaped together, and that terrific fright had suddenly roused in the white bird a renewed and fiercely reinforced antagonism for his successful rival. The whole event of his own mating with the dark duck had been swept away from his memory by the terror of the lynx's attack, back in the breeding grounds, when she had been so suddenly slaughtered. At intervals since, he had remembered innumerable tiny acts of rivalry and antagonism between himself and the pintail drake, and some similarity of emotion in the new panic he felt at the gun attack had awakened his enmity again.

The white drake had always been an outcast. His mallard mother had mated with a strange white bird, and of her clutch of seven nestlings, all but this one had been killed in the first few months of life. White individual mallards like this, with all the physical mallard characteristics but a wilder, more solitary, more adventurous spirit than any mallard ever had, are well known. This one, driven out by that fear of the stranger which marks not only wild creatures but human animals as well, had been forced away from the mallard community in which he had grown up and had attached himself domineeringly to the shy pintail group with which he had flown north. If his dark pintail mate had lived, he would have been accepted, and would have settled down among them. Now he was solitary again, proud and aggressive, looked at askance by the drakes, not wanted out of mating time by the ducks.

Ever since he had offered his courtship display to the pintail duck, he had felt a discontent, not at all appeased by accepting another mate. As the urgent fires of Spring died into the glow of Summer and passed to Autumn, he forgot his desire for the little duck but gradually acquired first a keen interest and then slowly an angry dislike of the drake who had mated with her.

As the flock sped through the rain-swept night over the sea, strange compulsions in him stirred irresistibly and caused him to glide out in front of his pintail rival and leap and play like a huge gnat in the watery light from a cloud-haunted moon. He flashed and dived at tremendous pace, then glided up again on wide-stretched white wings. This form of flying challenge, made so obvious to them all, first startled and then stirred the pintail drake to angry competition.

They were flying at a fast pace, and to spare energy for aerobatics was perilous. Other drakes, who might have joined the display had the flock been resting at some lake or creek, looked on querulously, but took no part in it. The formation swept on through the increasingly stormy night with the two birds jetting out in front, soaring, curving, and steeply diving, returning for periods to their places and then flying for a few miles steadily together, but ever and again breaking away for further wild evolutions.

All through the myriad forms of life, there comes this mingling, at times, of three instead of two—for the little pintail duck was riding now, near the front of the formation, where she had moved up on first noticing her mate commencing those strange and dangerous wheeling flights. In enticement or in defiance, there comes the sudden flash of eye to eye, and instantly tragedy is in the air. Many birds couple for life, but if one of the challengers dies, the survivor usually claims the female. All feathered creatures of the air are conscious of this, and though there was no time for fighting during migration over the sea, each of these drakes now wanted the other out of the way, and their increasingly daring and tiring pirouettes in front of the moving formation sought fatigue, collapse, and drowning of whichever proved the weaker.

Presently, the mere competition of grace-note flying was not enough to satisfy the antagonism both were developing. They had each become dangerously weary. The quarrel between them must be settled soon, or both might fall into the black and leaping water below. They lifted their feathered shoulders in sudden effort and flew out ahead of the rest with newly rapid wingbeats drawing them steadily away.

Soon, they were out of sight of the others, and out of sound of that great swishing of wings. They strove to pass each other, but flew shoulder to shoulder in the dark, their hearts beating huge with effort. Thrills of anger ran through each of them. They forgot the urge calling them southward, though they maintained the direction in which they had been flying. They forgot the thousands coming behind them. They were alone, and all that remained was to pierce the stormy and cold night air until only one survived in it. As the buffets of wind struck them, each watched for the other's fall.

The white mallard, heavier and stronger, began to show that he would be the eventual survivor. The pintail drake's long and slender wings struck the wind just as surely and as fast, and not one foot could the other bird gain in that tremendous and exulting race in the dark. But the white bird knew by a dozen little signs that his rival was weakening—the more anxious stretch of the long neck, the faintest flinching from the sudden gusts, a faint glaze on the dark, tormented eyes. Striving almost beyond endurance, the white mallard attempted to force the pace and draw ahead so as finally to exhaust his enemy to death.

It was then, far and uncertain across a tumultuous waste of seas, that they saw the light.

It was not the light of dawn, because it came and went, regularly flashing, then leaving the world black. It was too steady for lightning, repeating again and again its sudden message, and leaving the intervals between more black and menacing than before. Because light is life, the two birds turned toward it.

How distant it was, a pin point of yellow, coming and going and coming again. It seemed to grow no larger, though the pintail drake felt he had been flying toward it so long. There was a thick drizzling rain filling the air. It chilled him, seemed to present an impalpable mass against his breast and head, and dragged at his tucked-up feet. The white mallard was drawing ahead, inch by inch, and if he did that, the pintail could never survive.

If only he could reach the light. . . .

His wings lifted a little higher, thrashed down a little farther and a little faster, though the effort almost burst his heart. The wildness of the storm glided under his breast, bearing him up. He was flying badly, unevenly, ungracefully, but he was flying beat for beat with his rival, who, though striving to do so, had not the strength to lever himself forward any faster.

It had become a huge light now—a light showing from the head of a stone-built tower standing on pointed rocks over the outermost of which enormous seas were bursting. The light glowed yellow, showing a great path over the heaving water; then it blackened silently out; then it came glowing again. As the vast yellow beams of the lighthouse shot out, the pintail drake could see thousands of black dots whirling and sliding, diving and lifting, circling and almost standing still in the blinding glow, while others came pouring in from the darkness at the sides.

These black dots were small migrant birds, a great flock of which had been proceeding ahead of the wild ducks over the sea. They had come, in the baffling drizzle of thick rain, to the lighthouse and now were sweeping and circling about it, entranced by its intermittent beams of blinding light.

The two wanderers entered the full magic of the light bar, and everything suddenly ceased for them except the ecstasy and mystery of the light. Wild ducks are not usually caught in the enchantment of lighthouse beams as myriads of smaller birds are; when flying normally, these two would have passed over it. But now they were weary to the point of death, and in that exhausted state, the light, and the warmth which they always associated with light, completely compelled their course.

Sailing down the light beam, they flew so close to the great lantern in the tower's summit that only a sudden tail flicker saved them from dashing into the thick and shimmering glass; they worshiped it—and then it went out.

It was as if death had come suddenly—but then, with a staggering jolt, a ghastly spell had snapped and there was still time to get away. The two drakes circled wearily over the lighthouse, and below them in a gleam from the fitful moon that now seemed so pale, thousands of the little birds began to flee pell-mell, knocking into each other as if they were blind, some dropping stunned into the water or on the rocks, others going off at wild angles in panic chaos.

Then the silent yellow glory engulfed them again, sucked their spirits into itself, and drew them helplessly back to the tower. The whole zone of the light, as far as it could be followed stretching across the tumbling sea, was alive with little birds coming and going. Clouds of birds approached the lantern in an uninterrupted stream, most of them sweeping past on one side or the other like a swarm of bees, but one or two each second flying headlong against the glass and falling plummetlike into the dark below. The drops of rain in the light beam turned golden, the birds looked golden, and to add to all this loveliness, as they fluttered up the rays, many of them sang little snatches of song. Some seemed able to go right up to the glass and remain fluttering against it, gazing in, fascinated by its powerful rays.

The two drakes, despite a pervading terror, found themselves slowly sailing down toward the light. As they went, both saw a terrible thing. Far below, on a long tongue of rock where the leap and savage swirl of the waves could not reach, there were serried lines of little birds' bodies like windrows in sand. There must have been hundreds of the dead, and each moment, after striking the glass, more fell.

But the air was full of the living—full of them, diving and playing, and drunk with light. In the beam again now, the pintail drake felt himself part of that light, flowing, glowing, quivering as the rain poured through it in golden showers. He found himself again flying irresistibly toward the glass that looked so hard and smooth and beautiful. The light came from behind the glass, and if he could only fly on, he would touch the light itself.

His exhausted wings would hardly lift, and as he struggled forward among the mob of tiny birds, the mallard went past him, able now at last to win this terrible race over the sea. The white bird shone in the light that showed every proud feather, every lissome curve of neck and wing. He flew straight at the lantern like a white dart, the stretch and power of his beautiful wings carrying him triumphantly into the lead. He struck the glass with a thud, leaving a splash of blood, and as he folded his wings and hurtled down to join the windrows of dead upon the rock, once more the light went out.

21. *Poison Lake*

Just as the glory of the lighthouse beam turned to darkness, the pintail drake saw the land. Distant, over tossing crests and breakers, he glimpsed a huge hump of cliff and knew it, though he had never seen it before, for the landfall the wild ducks sought. Shocked by the crash of the white mallard only a foot or two ahead of him, the pintail slid at the last second round the lighthouse head and into the blackness.

Once more, for a moment, the deadly magic of the light was broken. For twenty wingbeats, the drake went jetting toward the cliff. Out of that land, as from the heart of some great, dark flower, came remembrance like a wild fragrance— remembrance of sunshine, food, happiness, and the content of lake-borne nights.

Then, high overhead, he heard the whispering of thousands of wings and recognized the sound as that of the passing of his own formation of wild ducks. From up there in the black dome of night came a thin, wild calling as the fliers in the darkness checked their places. Next moment, exactly as the lighthouse beam shone out again, the pintail drake struggled wearily up into the tail of that great procession. Even now, the light called him back, but a blind instinct stronger than death took him after the mate who had been his and the creatures of his own kind. As though it was his last effort, he spasmodically hauled himself over the cliffs and found a place among the youngest birds in the tail of the sky horde.

He had no idea how long they flew overland before they glided down to rest. Doggedly, he dragged himself along, stared at curiously by the proud and gleaming young birds of the year among whom he was flying. Once or twice, he staggered out of formation and managed to beat his way into it again. The night overland was gusty, black, and showery. Presently, he saw the leaders swoop downward, and he could hardly hold his wings out long enough to bear him onto the surface of an uncomprehended lake. He swallowed down some water and then sank into a sort of semiconscious trance.

It was afternoon when he awoke. The multitude of birds was quietly resting, and his mate was sailing a few feet from him, placidly watching him. Instantly, he was shaken by a flash of memory, in which the white mallard sailed at tremendous speed into the glass of the lighthouse and fell down among the rows of dead on the rock. The pintail drake stared round in alarm. He became uneasy and restless. He swam to the edge of the lake, ate hurriedly, drank, then surveyed the peaceful Autumn afternoon.

In the embrace of all this somnolent peacefulness, his alarm dwindled. Yet he still felt ill at ease. He got out of the water and began to wander round the edge of the lake. The leaves were turning color rapidly in night frosts, and they shone red and gold all around. Suddenly, the drake heard the faintest murmur of distant wings and looked round to see what birds were coming.

Over his head along the aerial birdway, whose easy route

made it common to many sorts of migrants, began an amazing pilgrimage. First of all came an unbroken and apparently quite unending stream of crows, flying steadily and quite silent except for the rush of their wings. They were not flying high, only about a hundred feet above the earth, and following its contours as they purposefully passed on their way. They were going over for a long while. After them came a great horde of thrushes, starlings, fieldfares, larks, finches, and robins. They had no appearance of haste, but there was no pause or deviation, and they gave the impression of being on a long journey easily within their power to accomplish. Some must certainly have been flying for many hours, probably since dawn. The weather was settled and fine after the rain of the night, conditions were mild, but the passing of this huge mob of various birds meant only one thing—that Winter was close behind them. In the thickest part of the movement, they came not merely flock after flock, but flock *above* flock, so that it was impossible, from the ground, to see the limits of the moving multitudes.

They must have numbered myriads of birds, yet they went by with hardly a sound except for the disturbance of the air. Just occasionally, there would be the *zip* call of a thrush or the chuckle of a fieldfare, cutting sharply into the whisper of the breeze and the blind lap of the waves on the lake shore. Over them was a lightly clouded sky, and the air seemed, through the warning of their going, already to move with a colder nip. Once, high overhead, a small flock of doves flew past, traveling much faster than the smaller birds below them, which they overtook and left behind. Now and again, too, a family of hawks, three or four birds together, would pass silently along on pointed wings, watching for weaklings who might fall out

of the migrating flocks, but afraid to attack the main formations while in such large numbers.

Stirred by this tremendous activity in the sky and moved by
a sense of urgency gathered from their wholesale flight from
Winter, the drake suddenly winged his way up toward them.
He passed between huge formations of birds speeding on their
journey and finally rose to a considerable height above the
passing multitudes. Looking down, he could now see the
great river valley, of which the lake was an offshoot. The valley
looked like a big ditch, with innumerable patches of little
square fields on either side. Greatly excited by watching the
migrants, the drake began to tumble about the sky, swooping,
plunging, and sweeping upward; and his antics brought scores
of other wild ducks off the lake to join him. As though in
commentary and approval of the continuous movement of
birds below them, two or three hundred ducks catapulted to
and fro, up and down, dancing in the air, catching the afternoon sunlight on gleaming heads and wings and bodies; nor
did they descend again till, in the early evening, the rushing
torrent of passing migrants finally ceased.

The pintail drake was very tired. Birds use relatively much
less energy when flying fast, which is why they travel at high
speed on long migration flights. On first getting into the air,
they use about five times as much effort as when in full flight,
and the evolutions the wild ducks had been performing, with
sudden speed variations making them beautiful, had called for
strength, judgment, and skill. When he dropped onto the lake
water again, his wings felt heavy and his mind confused.
Others who had been taking part in that wonderful winged
display also looked slack and heavy now they were at rest. They
seemed to have sunk into themselves and were markedly dif-

ferent from the rest of the alert and graceful pintails who crowded the surface in thousands.

The drake settled himself to rest and sleep, though this was the normal time for drinking and feeding. He sank into a sort of stupor which lasted all through the night. Usually, when he slept, some subconscious sense, common to all wild things, warned him of the condition of the world around. Without disturbing his rest, this strange extra vision made him aware whether his neighbors were tranquil or warned him instantly if an enemy approached too near by land, sea, or air. Tonight, because this awareness had deserted him, he slept badly, waking now and then in terror, only to sink into heavier sleep again.

Next morning, he was lethargic from having missed the night feed, yet unwilling to start looking for something to eat. His tongue was swollen, and he felt reluctant to fly. Others, also, were unwell, sitting heavily on the water, uninterested in events about them, showing no signs of the swift timidity that characterizes healthy pintails. The drake swam slowly about the lake, washed halfheartedly, and began to drink.

The lake water tasted peculiar and bitter. Beyond all capacity of the birds' knowledge, there was a reason for that deadly poisoned flavor. Two miles away, along a stream that drained into the lake, stood a great new factory, whose effluent, carrying dangerous metallic salts, was carried to the lake by the river water. The fish in the lake had been killed long ago, but the pondweeds, on whose tips and tender bulbous roots the wild ducks fed, seemed to thrive on the poison. There were luscious sedges, docks, grasses, and water plantains, some of them still juicy and cooling to throats already furred with metallic slime, and having begun at last to eat, the drake bolted them down avidly. But each was nourished on the poison already creeping with slow, chilling pain about his whole body, and that heavy meal made him feel more drowsy and sick than before.

The previous morning, while he had been sleeping off the effects of the overseas race, some of the young birds, hungry from their long flight, had gone adventuring over the neighboring fields. They had discovered an area where grain had been harvested, but where heavy gleanings had fallen among the stubble. They had stuffed themselves almost dangerously with ripe grain and flapped heavily back, their smug condition advertising to the others that rich food was to be had in quantity nearby. From that time, coveys of birds had been going continually to the grain fields.

The pintail drake, after resting for much of the day while a heavy Autumn rain was falling, joined one of these raiding parties toward evening. He flew laboriously, but he felt better, perhaps because of the cool washing of the rain over his feathers for several hours. The stubble field was full of rain pools which shone like splashes of melted lead among the dull gold, and he went first to one of these and drank. The water was sweet and clean, but the difference failed to teach him to avoid the lake water, since wild creatures cannot learn from deduction but usually only from experience.

The drink strengthened him at once, and he turned boldly to hunt the stubble for delicious golden grain. The ducks went systematically up and down, gormandizing, and calling at each rain-water pool that lay in their path to examine it minutely for the beginnings of edible life that comes almost immediately water settles on land. In the edge of one of these pools, the drake spied a young frog, very small and tender, and darted at it, but a feathered rush from his side beat him, and he turned in anger and saw his mate staring at him with intense satisfaction as the frog was assisted downward by a series of convulsive gulps. He was irritable, but not nearly so much as if the thief had been a drake or any other duck. The two birds stared at each other, recognizing but a little hostile. This sexless attitude of questioning companionship would remain with them, now, until next mating season, when they would pair again. In the Winter, they would know each other, prefer each other's company as a rule to that of the rest of the flock, but accept the relationship with doubt and frequent annoyance and certainly without chivalry or self-sacrifice.

Next morning, feeling much better for the healthy food and drink of the previous night, the drake stuffed at the lake feeding place and drank more than usual of the metallic water. That evening, following some inexplicable instinct, hundreds of the birds suddenly mounted the saffron-yellow sky and began to take up formation places for the next step of the migration journey. The drake saw them rise, and his wings flapped feebly in response, but he made no real effort to get off the water, for he was ill almost to death. The poison lake was doing its work, and not only with him. All round, scores of other birds slumped on the rippling surface, their feathers lying soggily against their bodies and giving an unnatural impression of thinness, their wings lank, their jaunty tails drooped almost onto the water.

The fliers swooped round and round uncertainly, quacking and piping noisily. They swept low across the lake, and again dozens of the victims' wings weakly flapped, as though some great magnet in the sky was drawing at them, but with not quite sufficient power. One or two birds did actually struggle into the air and fly a few yards, flopping down again with

lumpy splashes that told more sharply than anything else how
their condition had altered.

Scores of the flying birds from overhead began to alight
uncertainly on the lake again. But the clamor from the skies
redoubled, urgently recalling them; the great and compulsive
power that stimulates migration does not hesitate or weaken
because a few hundred die, and, indeed, in every year's migratory movements among birds, untold millions are fated never
to reach their longed-for destination. Enemies among the
animals, birds, fishes, and reptiles drag them down; man
slaughters them in hordes; wind, fog, hail, snow, and ice op-
pose them; many lose their way or are tempted or driven from
their course; they strike high buildings or telephone wires or
electric pylons, or they rush bewildered against lighted sky-
scrapers in cities; a change of weather completely deprives
them of natural food and they starve, or poisoned water deci-
mates them. A million dead at a time have been seen in only
one place after an unseasonable storm of wet and heavy snow;
yet that snowstorm covered fifteen hundred square miles!

As those who had descended again on the lake once more
took wing, the urgency of the calling from the skies became
pitiful. But the heavy and sodden figures on the water now
gave no sign of response. Far over them against the evening
clouds, the mass of the migrants slipped swiftly into traveling
order and began to wing away southward, and presently the
last sound of their going died from the air.

The pintail drake was aware that his mate was slumped on
the water near him, in no better case than he. That night was
a fog of listlessness shot with terrible and cramping pains, sick-
ness, cold, and terror, which each bird had to bear in loneliness
that was in no way mitigated by the nearness of others in

similar plight. When the morning sun touched the water, three birds lay on the margin of the lake, in water an inch or two deep, dead or dying. They were drooped and still, and the head of one was submerged.

A current in the lake now began to have an effect on the survivors, who were too ill to eat, drink, or even maintain their position. They drifted unaware, caught in the flow from the poisoned stream, and so, bunched miserably and helplessly together, they were very slowly carried round the lake to the opposite side, where the river continued its course. More died during the day, but over a hundred of them were carried into the river course that afternoon and began to float along it, turning round and round, bumping each other, only their drooping heads upheld from the surface showing that they were still alive.

They were floating north, back along the route they had already come. And the weather was changing. The sky, from soft Autumn tints, was growing steely, and the air had become bitterly cold. Perhaps it was the warning of this pursuing Winter that had sent the other migrants so uncompromisingly onward in their flight from the cold.

For a part of a day and a night and another day, the victims drifted slowly northward along the river. Sometimes, they struck overhanging branches. Sometimes, they were caught by beds of waterweed or rushes. Some dying instinct to keep together enabled them feebly to kick their way clear, when they abandoned themselves again, a dark and silent group, to the gentle embrace of the water.

On that nightmare journey, many let their heads drop under the surface and died. About forty were left by the evening of the second day.

22. Southward

THAT EVENING, the drake felt much better. He drank feverishly. The water had lost its sharp metallic taste, for the poison was left in the lake, and now they were in completely untainted river once more. They all drank, and ate sparingly, their tongues being swollen. Some of them tried to wash and tidy their draggled and dirty feathers.

One more died during the night, but the rest were so much better next morning that several were able to fly. During that day, with the swift and sudden powers of recovery belonging to most wild creatures, they became normal again, ate and drank heavily, and preened their feathers constantly, passing each feather sharply through an oil-loaded bill. At intervals, they slept. In the evening, after a last drink and feed, the little duck quacked loudly and imperatively, all heads lifted, and she shot up into the sky, followed by the rest. Immediately taking up long-distance formation, with the duck and her mate in the lead, they turned south and began to fly steadily down the miles that separated them from the vanished squadron.

It was a dark night, without moon or stars. Heavy and immovable clouds filled the sky. It was intensely cold, with a

biting wind out of the north that whined behind the fliers
and against which as they flew they ruffled the down that
imprisoned an insulating blanket of warmer air between their
flesh and the gale.

For two hours, the birds flew swiftly, and as they went, the
air seemed to grow colder. Then they came to an area where
an upcurrent of air, still racing from the north, seemed to
lift them on their way. And then the hail began.

Just as the sleeting storm started, they overtook a big, straggling mob of smaller migrants, cheeping to one another as
they poured through the dark. The wild ducks heard and
vaguely saw them and rose to pass over them, with stabbing
fusillades of white coming down on a long slant, overtaking and
striking at them. This was large hail, and the stones drummed
on the flying ducks and pierced cruelly into the feathers of the
smaller wayfarers below. Their mild and cheerful twittering
changed to an outcry of terror; dozens were seen dropping
away from the rest, beaten, damaged, probably hurtling down
to death, while the remainder skated downward in wildest
alarm, to try to find shelter on the ground. They were passing
over a plain with hardly a bush to be seen; hundreds of the
tiny birds would certainly be killed. The wild ducks flew on
indifferently; they were wet, bruised, and too much obsessed
with their own troubles to be aware of those of others.

They went along at a rapid rate, bunched well together,
and calling constantly so as to keep close, for the hailstorm, the
rain that succeeded it, and the darkness showed them their
neighbors only as vague blotches of black in a black mist. They
felt now that they were fleeing from some tangible enemy in
the north behind them, an enemy compounded of icy cold,
fear, hunger, and thirst. The cold winds ruffled feathers of

breast and back as they flew, requiring constant adjustments
of balance and wing stroke, and the invisible world below
brought to them strange smells and sounds as they passed,
scents of forests and brake and field, variations in the whistling
of the wind as it struck trees and hillsides or fell booming
into valleys.

There was a moment that night when, with joyful recognition, all were aware that they had rejoined the great river
valley up which they had flown northward. Nothing was to be
seen but rain-swept blackness, but they could smell the cold
freshness of the river that was different from other rivers over
which they had passed, and they could sense the rebound of
the wind from contours they could not view but could remember.

Just ahead of them, they could recall a city round which they
had made a big detour on the journey north. Each bird had
seen from a distance and now recalled the outline of that
smoky sprawl of buildings. Now, in the small hours of the
morning, experience told them there was no danger from a
city, and they rose higher to pass directly over it.

Presently, looking down, the pintail drake saw myriads of
shadowy irregularities where the canyons of the streets divided
the black and crouching masses of the buildings. There were
a few golden squares of lighted windows, and apparently sus-
pended in the sky straight ahead was a blazing dome of light,
the neon-illuminated tower of some public building. Down
in the streets, a solitary car moved slowly, the beams from its
headlights questing forward like the bright antennae of some
night-hunting monster.

In an uninhabited bend of the river, the squadron of wild
ducks alighted as morning was breaking, wild and misty, along

the edge of a ridge of hills. But they had no sooner skimmed the water with their feathered breasts than they raced up again into the air, never even stopping, and pelted away at the very top of their speed. There was not a sign of anything to alarm them back there where a few agitated ripples alone showed that they had been. The river lolled slowly along between high reed beds, desolate and empty. Yet, as they vanished into the distant sky, a tousled fellow in a faded beret straightened himself, cursing, among the rushes; by his side was a strange, multibarreled gun set up on a stand concealed among the muddy growths, and a yellow cur whose ribs showed through his hide snuffled cautiously behind. Farther back still was a heap as big as a dining table of mallard ducks, their brown backs and long wings flung anyhow. One of the vivid green heads still moved feebly.

The pintails raced on for ten miles or more and then gladly descended on a fresh reach of river, this time really free of the terrible creature Man. It was a sullen-looking place, where a considerable tributary joined the main stream. The waters splashed turgidly together, and the muddy yellow current of the tributary could be distinguished on one side or the other for some distance. Dead-looking branches overhung the stream; ashore, there was a wild tangle of brownish thorny trailers shot with dying grasses and weeds.

A quarter of a mile back along the tributary stream, the bank rose in a steep, almost mountainous bluff, strikingly marked by a group of gnarled trees. The wild ducks found that the muddy water of this fast-flowing stream was filled with water insects, probably displaced by the floodwater from the night of storm over the distant hills. The birds began to wander upriver, eating and drinking as they went.

The pintail drake found himself presently, out ahead of the rest, bobbing on the river just under that clump of ancient trees. He was so intent on dabbling in the water picking up food that he did not, for some time, examine his surroundings. Such an omission may at any time cost a bird its life. Presently, staring about, he saw an ancient structure of sticks, a sort of wild platform raggedly jammed in a tree crotch over his head and straggling out insecurely from the trunk. It was perhaps a yard wide and almost a foot thick.

At the first glimpse of it, the drake hopped out of the water into the air and sped only a foot above the river back toward the flock. He was going at tremendous speed, every line in his stretched form shouting an alarm, and the others whipped up and turned with him, flying out of that place as though the ultimate of all terrors was behind them. What the drake had seen and recognized was a raven's nest, and as the birds in full flight, still only inches from the water, tore down the river, a great raven sailed overhead, turned on a tremendous wing whose purple iridescence shone rustily, realized that his chance of a weakling had gone, and swung round toward his nest. His flapping wings measured more than a yard from tip to tip. As he landed on the platform of sticks, he croaked hoarsely and as it seemed derisively, but the ducks were out of sight.

They flew nervously along the river for several miles, skirting villages, sweeping low over promising lonely places where the conditions seemed favorable for resting, but each time climbing again, their two recent frights having made them almost afraid to descend anywhere. Finally, shortly before midday, they settled quietly in a marsh through which the river divided into a dozen skeins of muddy water. A pale sun was showing, and much of the bitter coldness of the night had gone in muggy Autumn weather, but ground and air felt damp and spent. The birds uneasily stared about them, swimming quickly to and fro in a group, listening, prepared at any movement to fly again. Gradually, they settled to repose, and for the rest of the day, they remained sleeping or watching, and in the night, they fed.

They seemed to have lost the urge to hurry south after the main flock. Several days were spent in that marshy bend of the river's course. One morning, the pintail drake and duck, wandering together, found a hump of diseased wood at the foot of a willow and stood staring at it. The duck tentatively struck it with her bill, breaking away a piece of rotten tinder. Then both began steadily breaking open the swollen, soft blister on the base of the trunk, pausing every now and then to smell or listen to something inside.

A final blow knocked away a big piece of brown wood, and immediately a swarm of ants was visible. The little duck squatted awkwardly down against the base of the tree and began to move her wings and ruffle her feathers gently over the excited and racing ants, many of which carried eggs in their jaws. Numbers of them at once rushed up into her feathers. To assist them, she began dabbling at the thicker clusters of insects with her bill, picking up numbers of them and jerkily throwing them under her half-opened wings, first on one side, then on the other. The drake watched, interested; he tried to squat down too, but there was not room for two of them, and after some desultory attempts to pick up some of the ants, he accidentally swallowed one or perhaps it ran down his throat, and he then stood back, ruffled and angry, several feet away, observing the performance.

The duck went on busily and apparently enjoyably fluffing

herself over the ants, tossing them under her wings, and dabbling about in the nest to stir them to further activities. They
did not seem to sting her, and it appeared that this strange
ant bath was regarded by her as a comfort or a luxury. Perhaps
the ants, wandering in her feathers, ridded her of smaller
parasites. Perhaps she had a queer liking for their pungent
smell. At least she was doing what wild ducks not infrequently
will do, and after she was satisfied, she fluffed her feathers hard
to shake out the now unwanted guests and then flew high in
the air, curvetting and circling as if in a transport of new
delight.

That night, the warmer weather changed again. It became
oppressive and thick, and a smell as of stale smoke tainted the
air and gathered in acrid power. There was no sign of moon
or stars, not a vestige of light anywhere. The wild ducks noticed with apprehension that their small sounds of movement,
the splash as they dipped to feed, and their occasional quiet
calls to one another became heavily muffled. A thick, cold,
clinging white fog was descending all over the countryside,
and it grew so dense that, when vague paleness drifted through
it indicating morning, though the birds were mobbed together
and almost touching, they could not clearly see each other,
only a vague form here and a feathered shoulder there.

Alarmed by their delay and suddenly frantically desiring
to get south into a climate and a home where they would be
away from these ugly changes, they flew up into the clinging
and blinding thickness and turned south, calling uneasily to
try to keep in touch with birds they could not see.

23. *The Blinding Fog*

THE LITTLE GROUP of birds went through the fog at the top of their migration speed, not flying joyfully and easily but nervously alert. Fog meant peril to them all. The whole formation might lose its way, since objects seen through a thick and drifting curtain can easily be mistaken. Individual birds were in constant risk either of losing the rest or of flying so close to a neighbor that a mile-a-minute collision might result in fatal damage. In addition, the clinging damp penetrated their down as no rain could do and chilled them. Birds' eyes are sensitive to certain light rays which human eyes do not record, and birds can see through fog to some degree, but not so well in drizzling rain such as was falling as these wild ducks swept on their way through rolling and heavy masses of yellowish-white vapor.

Their course, which they selected instinctively because generations of their kind had safely used it, lay now over a mountain watershed. In the soggy mistiness, there was a momentary peril that some faulty choice of route might dash them against an unseen pinnacle of rock or bring them flying into a bare hillside. With a wild cry and a sudden lean of wings, the leaders rushed sideways along the face of one such declivity that upreared not more than a yard before them through a rent blown in the foggy curtain, and the rest, instantly translating the warning note, swerved away after them. They knew at once that they must be off their course, but now they were forced to follow the contour of the mountainside, flying blind, seeking with all their senses tense for a warning of rocks ahead, conscious that any moment might send them smashing into a cliff face.

Cautiously, they rose higher and higher to clear such obstacles, but the higher they got, the less chance was there to recognize again the contour of the fleeing country below and correct their veer away from the southward line. The leaders, calling down the line, began to swing round in a curve to try to find the river valley on the other side of the watershed that would lead them over the last stretch of their journeying.

Descending a little, thrusting their heads forward to try to see the first vague shape of the land beneath, they skimmed over a dimly outlined mountaintop, then swooped over the edge of a precipice and dived straight down, following the shape of the land, into a valley, whizzing down hundreds of feet almost vertically. The fog was a little thinner here, and they could see well enough where they were going. The valley was strange to them, but it ran in the direction they wanted to go, and they raced along it over half-seen trees. Then came a rolling sweep of vapor, and everything vanished again. Immediately, the birds began to rise on a long slant, every nerve quivering.

The pintail duck, flying among the leaders, with the drake next on her right, could catch only occasional vague glimpses of him, though he was so near that their wings almost touched in the downward beats that drove them along. She saw at times the feathery sweep of his pinion, instantly withdrawn into invisibility; once, as the fog thinned, she noticed his head stretched out; then everything was gone, and his presence was known only by the steady undulations of the air and the sound of his passage.

The fog thickened as they flew on, and nothing could be seen ahead, while the ground below vouchsafed only the most abrupt and uncertain outlines seen and lost in a second and seeming to sway in the billows of the mist. Suddenly, utterly without warning, the little duck found herself looking into the round eyes and over the hooked, cruel beak of an eagle blundering along on enormous wings—a head-on collision seemed already to have happened, yet by a twist of one or both birds she scraped past under his breast feathers and heard him smash into the bird on her left. Both went rolling helplessly down into the swirl of fog below, injured or killed. The duck, terrified almost to paralysis, beat her wings wildly trying to regain her place among birds she could not see, whose formation had burst into tatters as each flier frantically wheeled aside from that enormous shadow that had passed so terribly through their midst. Calling, adjusting, redressing their line blindly as best they could, the ducks fled onward, afraid to stop.

An hour later, the fog began to thin again. It wreathed and blew about in stupendous billows filling half the sky; now it was blinding, now they could see for a mile and the land below was dimly visible, rolling hill country heavily covered with woods, which they had never seen before. Presently there was only a wet and clinging mist that turned every contour to softest, chilliest gray and disclosed a smoky world of gray-green and gray-brown.

Instinct, and the distant presence of a ghostly sun, told the wild ducks that they were flying south toward the light by which all their daily actions were measured, but this was not the familiar river valley of their northward flight. They pressed on, the miles reeling away behind them, and came by evening to a desolate pond on which they slept for two or three hours, after feeding, and then, in the misty night, flew up and on again.

Just before dawn, the landscape, palely outlined by a small moon, looked suddenly familiar, though still the great river which should have guided them was not to be found. Another river wound beneath them through a great indigo plain from which woods stood up in solid masses of black. A marshy place where the river spread among reeds tempted them down to feed again and, as they thought, to rest through the daylight hours before continuing a night flight southward.

There was ample food in the rushy lanes through which the water stealthily wandered, but these were so narrow that the birds divided up into threes and fours to explore them for insects and succulent weeds. The drake and his mate kept together, and he swam along in the lead, with several yards dividing him from her. Everything seemed very tranquil, and their normal extreme care in a strange place finally gave way to a half-watchful lazy enjoyment of the rest after the long flight and the protection from misty air afforded by the high banks of reeds.

For an hour or more, they loitered, feeding and drinking and drowsing. They could hear small, faint sounds from neighboring channels in the reeds where other ducks were passing, seeking comfortable corners to rest through the day, whose brightness was now showing watery and dispersed in the eastern sky. The fog was thickening again, blowing silently in on a chill breeze, and rapidly the outlines of things grew vague, wavered, and disappeared. Although only six or eight feet from his mate, the drake could not see her; the mist thinned and she was visible again; then gone; then she appeared once more.

He saw with alarm that she was sitting very stiffly on the water, listening. Something had startled her. He stared about him sharply. Through the rushes and waterweed, something black was drifting in the foggy haze on his other side. He thought it was a log, but it was the prow of a punt carefully concealed in a draping of weed. He watched it nervously. He heard the duck suddenly scutter up into the air, and a roar of wings behind her, and he himself was flying up and up. A red stab leaped toward him from the punt, where a man lying in the bottom had an old gun aimed over the bow.

The drake felt a searing blow along his back, his wings flapped straight above him and ceased to support him, and he fell down twenty feet of air onto the water only a yard from the boat. As he heard the man clamber to his feet to look overside, the drake swam in abject terror against and underneath the bow of the flat punt and clung there, his heart clumping enough to blind him and that burning agony across his back making him stiffen and slacken his neck continually, though he dared not make any move of wings or tail that would betray his presence by a sound.

The man swore, peered this way and that in the fog, splashed the water within a foot of the drake's head, and then the boat was paddled slowly round. As it went, the drake clung to it, feverishly keeping under the cover of its sloped bow. The boat began very slowly to move forward toward a patch of reeds and was driven round them, the man beating at them with a long stick. The sound of each blow and the rush of the bending reeds caused the drake almost to die of terror, for the stick was whizzing just over his body, and the man's hairy and dirty hand, holding it, came intermittently into the bird's view.

With a sudden red-hot agony, the drake experimentally moved his wings. They were not broken; the muscles were not cut; but as they moved, a warm trickle of blood overflowed down his side from the raw scratch where the lead had scored along the skin of his back. He was stupefied with fear; he thought, each time that hand and stick came out, that they were reaching for him.

He clung helpless under the boat's edge, the water almost submerging him each time the man moved, rocking the little punt. Tramping feet, divided only by an inch of board from the drake's cowering and pain-shot body, told him that the man had come to that side. The old wildfowler's mind was reminding him of the habitual cunning of wounded birds. With a grunt, he reached a hand over the punt's edge and began to feel along the water at the bows to see if the duck he had hit was hiding there.

24. Safe

THE HAND joggling through the water and feeling under the overhang of the punt came nearer. The pintail drake seemed to shrink, yet however small he became, he knew that nothing could stop that naked thing from touching his feathers. Then the poking grip, the force tearing him from his hiding place.

As the first cringing feather registered a touch, the drake sprang forward and into the air. His back felt as if a red-hot iron pressed on it, but the greater terror cast out the less and he was able to fly, to crack away that paralysis which had immobilized him. There was a commotion and a shout behind him, the *bang* of a gun, and whining lead wailed past him. Then he was zigzagging all over the sky, untouched, almost dissolved with shock and fear, and the punt had vanished below in the thick mist that shrouded everything and completely hid the ground from his view.

He fled at tremendous speed, still wildly flickering about to escape imaginary pursuit, utterly unconscious of the way he was going. After a minute, he straightened into arrowy flight, and not till half an hour had put thirty miles between him and the place of that deadly attack did he pause to consider his route. Immediately, he found a fresh cause for alarm.

He was utterly alone, and wild ducks, so accustomed to the social atmosphere of the flock, seek it again with ever-increasing urgency if they are isolated far enough away not to know where their fellows may be found.

The drake remembered how his mate and the rest had exploded into the sky just before he was hit and fell. They had gone in all directions and vanished into the mist. It was impossible to know where he could find them. All round him, the fog was clinging in wet, close whiteness that did not give a visibility of a yard. He had no idea how far down the ground lay under him or where he was heading, and the firmament felt so empty that there might not have been another bird in creation. Instead of the gay calling of his kind for miles across a sky-flung echelon or even the crowded wingbeats of the little squadron that had been left behind at the poison lake, he was solitary, unprotected by others' vigilance, unable to share with them the mysterious responsibility for finding the way over country he had never passed before and could not see even now.

Rising higher in circles, he began to "feel" for the urge that silently calls migrating birds on their unseen paths through the sky. It was no matter now of recognizing land contours, for beneath his tucked-up feet there was nothing but dully drifting grayness. Above him, pressing down on him as he flew, was the same enveloping fog, shutting out all chance of direction from the sun and even preventing any turning toward the point of greatest lightness, for here the thickly filtered light was equally feeble on every side. Perhaps his questing eyes possessed a visual perception of electromagnetic radiation, which would enable him by sight to distinguish between land and water and between the brightness hidden to the south and the relative darkness of the north. At least, after circling uncertainly for some minutes, he turned southward and began to fly with a long, steady wingbeat through the rolling vagueness.

As he went, his back felt stiff and horribly sore where the lead had ripped through the feathers and scored a line across the skin. It had bled only a little, and then the blood had congealed over the wound. But though no serious harm had been done, the exquisite balance of the wing strokes was affected, and after a few hours, the drake was forced to go cautiously down to seek a place to rest. There were fields under him, gray and desolate, and he sped along only twenty feet above them, peering painfully at them through the mist. With a jump that felt as if it broke his wound open afresh, he jerked up to miss some woods that suddenly loomed black immediately before him, and skimmed along over the tree-tops. Before he could stop, he had passed a little glade with a natural pond in it, and an attempt to bank round on one wing alarmed him with a fresh reminder of how hurt and stiff his back had become. While mechanically flying in a straight line with regular movements, he could go along in mere discomfort, but this gyration almost flung him to disaster. He limped down onto the water and sat there, swaying, looking uneasily round.

The pond was quite small, only about twenty feet across, and shallow because of years of accumulation of dead leaves, which stained the water a darkish brown. Bushes crowded right down to the water's edge, and the drake kept peering sharply about, conscious of the great dangers that could come from such proximity. He listened. The wood was still but for the almost imperceptible stirrings of leaves on the ground in the wayward breaths of air that moved the mist to and fro. He smelled the air, but there was nothing in it except the faintly decaying taints of Autumn. He fidgeted his wings to try to ease the soreness of his back. For a long time, although he was deathly weary, he remained with every nerve alert, trying to discover the whereabouts of any danger.

The place seemed utterly tranquil. The drake jerked himself upright as he began to slip into semiconsciousness and rest. Still there was no sound anywhere. Presently, he was sleeping, brokenly, uneasily, constantly awaking with a start and seeking about for perils. Alone, he was thousands of times more vulnerable than when with the great flock with which he had left the northland. For wild ducks in numbers so contrive their rest that some are awake all the time; moreover, many creatures which are unwilling to attack a flock will snap up a solitary bird.

When it was dark, the drake drank, ate, and went cautiously ashore to seek for more solid food. The mist was still thick and the night moonless. He heard some creature blundering through the bushes a hundred yards away and turned and fled back to the pond. But it was so small that there was no safety there as there would have been in the middle of a bigger sheet of water. All the time, he had to keep ready to leap into the air. It was too dark to see whether a fox was creeping near on padded feet or whether some hunting bird was gliding down through the trees. Several times that night, he heard the big creature that had startled him; it was going systematically about among the bushes, probably covering every yard of a customary hunting trail. Once, when it was almost out of earshot, there was a sudden splash on one side of the pond. Stiffly erect, ready for flight, the drake listened for the first ripple of water that would tell of something drawing near. But there was no ripple, no sound, no further disturbance of that sort. Immediately afterward, there was a rush of wings and a sort of stifled whistle, and the wings went away again. No owl would have made that peculiar wingbeat. What was it? What had happened over there where the splash had sounded and where afterward there was that sinister silence? The drake remained tense. Presently, to his increasing alarm, there came the smell of blood, thick and rank, mixed with the sour smell of the leafy pond water. Something had been killed over there in the dark and had been taken away.

Eventually, he settled down to rest again, in the same uneasy way as before, with every instinct alert even while he slept. In the morning, his back was stiff and any movement of his wings hurt him badly. He spent that day lurking on the edge of the pond beneath some overhanging brambles, so as not to be seen by animals on land or birds passing in the sky. He got colder and colder, partly through stiffness and lack of movement and partly because the fog was clearing away and giving place to leaden skies beneath which a shrill breeze went screeching by. There was hardly any food in that little pond, and frightened explorations among the bushes, and even frantic periods of digging and scratching among the leaves, disclosed nothing edible. Yet the drake was afraid to fly because of the hurt on his back.

That night, however, he managed to take wing and journeyed in considerable pain for several hours. Then he found a streamlet and shrank down in the reeds to rest, feeling as though he could never fly again. For two or three days, still without any recognition of the land over which he flew and without sighting either his own or any other flock of wild ducks, he traveled south, guided by instinct, but constantly frightened by his loneliness. The pain on his back gradually faded from his consciousness as the flesh wound healed, though he felt the cold there sharply where the down had been raked away.

Another danger began to threaten him. Birdways used on migration are not the result of chance; they have been chosen and are constantly corrected in detail to give the maximum number of safe resting places where adequate food can always be found. Flying parallel to the great river valley along which he and the others had gone northward in the Spring, the drake was like a human traveler who abandons a main road with its hotels and makes his way across country where no proper provision exists for meals and rest on the way. Sometimes, he had to fly for twelve or fifteen hours before daring to alight. Often, his resting places proved full of sudden terrors to send him into the sky before he had made recovery from a long spell of journeying at high speed. Ponds that looked secret and rich proved barren of food, except for a few shriveled mouthfuls, or were visited by animals or hunting birds in escaping from which the drake almost lost his life more than once.

Increasingly miserable and frightened in his solitary state, even now not fully replumaged after his molt, hungry, weary because of too extended flights and the unremitting haunting fear of resting properly lest some killer approach before he had regained alertness, the drake lost weight and condition. His feathers that had been so sleek became harsh, his eye feverish, all his movements spasmodic. A compelling instinct turned his head south and seemed to drag him along through the air with ever less time for rest as he grew more and more in need of it. Some inner sense warned him that, though he was overstraining his powers, it was better to do so than to delay an hour longer than need be a reunion with others of his kind. A little longer alone, trying to protect himself and keep alert night and day, and fatigue would make him fall victim to one of the enemies of land, water, or air whose shadowy presences increasingly threatened him as his reactions to danger dulled.

One night, as he slept, he drifted too close to a tangled bank, and a young fox that had been standing in the shadows, patiently watching, miscalculated by inches a leap into the shallow water. The drake found himself flying before he knew he had wakened; the fox's snout had touched him, and the great snap of those powerful jaws had sent a puff of stinking breath all over him. He flew on and on all through the next day of blinding rain, and in the afternoon, as he skimmed low over a marsh looking for somewhere to alight, a poacher's gun banged only a few yards under his feet. The shot went whistling through the air all around, missing him by a miracle but so filling him with panic that he lost all sense of time and place. He began to fly suddenly, not with the steady, tireless beat of migration, but with the utmost effort of which his overtired wings were capable. Instead of following the contour of the world below, he went arrow-straight, sometimes almost touching hilltops, sometimes high across valleys. He did not turn aside to skirt a village, but passed so low over the roofs that a boy with a catapult sent a small round stone hissing between hard-driven wing and outstretched neck.

The whole sky and all the earth seemed to the drake to be one frightening mob of enemies. He tried to go faster and could not. He expected more stones every minute, and more shots, though now the village was ten miles behind and no

sign of human habitation could be seen on the gray countryside. The very spears of rain, innumerable and irresistible,
seemed to threaten him.

The sodden, cold ground flew by just under him at sickening speed, but panic would not let him stop. Then a wooded
bluff on the horizon on his right twanged a familiar nerve, and
he swung toward it as though there alone he might find escape
from the horrors which pursued him. The bluff had the shape
of a crouching lion, and he knew it well, but could not remember, in his fear and the creeping fatigue that was slowing his
wingbeats, where it was or why he recognized it. But something about it, a longing to find something known after all
this wandering alone over strange places, as well as an alarmed
discovery that he could hardly fly more than another mile or
two, made him begin to glide down toward the bluff, hoping
to find water there. He was parched with thirst, and lack of
food enfeebled him.

Something moved among the trees—a dog—and this new
terror unloosed a final little burst of strength in his failing
wings. He sailed high over the bluff, and as he did so, the
whirring rain ceased as he raced through the edge of its area,
and a glitter of watery sun showed on the other side of the
hill.

To the drake, it was as though that glimmer of Autumn
sunlight had created a complete new world. For beyond the
bluff, he knew every delicate curve and changing shade of
color. He was too weary to recall why or when he had known
it, but this was territory with which he had been quite familiar
the previous Winter. Somehow gathering hope and encouragement from familiarity, he beat his way slowly onward, for now
he knew he need not look for a place to rest—on ahead, he

could not tell how far, was somewhere that would give food, drink, and perfect peace. Flying heavily along, almost half asleep on the wing, but with a blessed sense of being in a world he knew, with dangers all shut out, he plodded wearily through the air for mile after mile.

Far ahead, shining, a tiny patch of gold upon the drab of the darkening afternoon, he saw a lake and with a great throb knew that his quest was ended. As he flapped nearer, almost too spent to cover the last mile, he could see the dark trees that fringed it, and so, at last, holding out his wings that tried to droop, he glided swifter and swifter down onto its lovely and rippling surface.

The impetus of his glide carried him onward through the water a few yards, into a backwater hidden from the rest of the lake. Although he could scarcely move, he knew now that he was safe, and he paddled stiffly along the backwater looking for a place his memory knew, where he could hide and sleep as long and as safely as he wished.

Suddenly, he stopped and stiffened, staring at a strange new beautifully plumaged female who was watching him from the reeds. She squattered out and turned to swim frightened away—then looked back, came round in a tearing circle, and, using her wings to help her almost race across the surface of the water, she came close to him and sat quite still within a foot of his exhausted body. It was the mate to attract whom he had uttered his first mating whistle on this very lake in the Spring that seemed such a lifetime ago. She uttered a low quack and turned with him beside her toward a tiny creek into the reeds from which she had emerged. As he very slowly followed her, he became aware that the rushes were alive with a group of that flight of birds with whom he had flown south, and then he knew that all this struggle and questing were over at last. Here they were safe; here everything was familiar, and there was no need to stream away across the sky looking for anything any more. Or so it seemed as he swam after his mate toward the shelter he had known for so many months before the struggle of the northward flight all began.

He paused just as he was passing into the deep hiding of the reeds. Far along the backwater, beyond the corner on which he had stopped, he could see the banks grow steeper, crowned by woven reed screens. Something uneasy stirred in his mind. He had long ago forgotten the metal ring on his leg, which he had got by venturing too far along this backwater and into the duck decoy. Yet some instinct was trying to warn him. Far along there, he saw three or four ducks quietly feeding. They were not members of the flock he had traveled with; they were strangers to him, and he had no desire to make an acquaintance with them then. But that was because his fatigue had momentarily killed the curiosity which is a part of all wild things' nature.

He did not see the man hiding behind the screens, with the white dog at his heel. The drake turned slowly and moved into the semidarkness and safety of the rushes, where he settled down at once to sleep, his mate close beside him. He forgot about those interesting strange ducks at the mouth of the decoy—he could not know they were tame ducks, placed there to tempt others into the net for ringing, checking, and release.

But, later, when he was refreshed and fed and had forgotten all his fears, he saw them there again, and that day he was not so cautious. That is how I got to know him again, checked his number, and how this tale of some of his adventures came to be written.